Agricultural Atlas of Nebraska

Agricultural Atlas of Nebraska

Project Director
MERLIN P. LAWSON

Edited by
JAMES H. WILLIAMS
DOUG MURFIELD

Foreword by
JAMES H. ZUMBERGE

Cartographer
JOHN D. MAGILL

University of Nebraska Press • Lincoln and London

Research Assistants
JACQUELINE SMITH
STEVEN SOBERSKI

Publishers on the Plains
UNP

Copyright © 1977 by the University of Nebraska Press
All rights reserved
Manufactured in the United States of America

Library of Congress Cataloging in Publication Data

Main entry under title:

Agricultural atlas of Nebraska.

   1. Agriculture—Nebraska—Maps. 2. Agriculture—
Economic aspects—Nebraska. I. Lawson, Merlin P.,
1941– II. Williams, James H., 1918– III. Murfield, Doug,
1937–
G1451.J1A3 1976   912'.1'338109782   76–16169
ISBN 0–8032–0894–4

Cover photograph reproduced by courtesy of the Nebraska Game and Parks Commission.

Color photographs reproduced by courtesy of the
following: pages 1, 13, 27, 37, 77, 93, and 107, the
Nebraska Game and Parks Commission; page 18, D.
T. Lewis; and page 99, the Nebraska Farmer.

Black and white photographs reproduced by courtesy
of the following: pages 3 and 42, the Soil Conservation Service, U.S. Department of Agriculture; pages
44, 49, 62, 64, 71, 83, 85, 86, and 103, the Nebraska
Farmer; pages 69 and 78, the Nebraska Game and
Parks Commission; and page 75, the Nebraska Crop
Improvement Association.

CONTENTS

FOREWORD

Because the majority of Americans have enjoyed an abundance of relatively cheap food in great variety, they have come to take agricultural production for granted. They have seen tremendous surpluses pile up beyond the capacity of federal and private storehouses, and they have seen the United States send free grain to hungry nations all over the world. But all that has changed. We are moving from surplus to shortage insofar as the world food supply is concerned. Unless the agricultural technology of the United States and other countries can be pushed beyond its present capacity, death by starvation will sooner or later be the fate of millions of human beings. It was agriculture that made civilization possible in the beginning and it is agriculture that may save it in the end.

Those of us who are not directly involved in agriculture should be grateful that the work of one American farmer can feed fifty people. There was a time before the dawn of civilization when all able-bodied men, women, and children were engaged in gathering food or hunting wild game merely to avoid starvation. There was no time to contemplate the wonders of the universe, compose great music, or create masterpieces of art. None of these cultural advances became widespread until after man learned to domesticate animals and till the soil so as to assure himself and his family an adequate supply of food. The survival of civilization depends on a high level of agricultural productivity all around the world. Just to keep pace with the growing demand, production will have to be higher than we've ever known before.

The University of Nebraska, through its Institute of Agriculture and Natural Resources, has an opportunity to make a significant impact on world food problems. Through research in all areas that bear on the production of food from both plants and animals, and through the rapid delivery of this new knowledge to the farmer and the rancher, the agriculture and natural resources component of the university could be the most profitable investment of tax dollars ever undertaken by the state legislature. Nebraska's potential for increased agriculture production is enormous. The ingredients for greater agriculture production—fertile soils, good climate, and abundant water—are available and, when brought together with the technical knowledge from research and the hard work of a hearty people, will continue to reap rewards for the state and its inhabitants.

This agricultural atlas of Nebraska is the work of many people at the University of Nebraska and reflects the partnership between the university and the agricultural industry of the state. It serves two functions. First, it shows the enormous growth in diversity and productivity in Nebraska since agricultural practices were established more than a century ago. Second, it stands as a baseline against which future trends can be measured.

Those who are engaged in planning for Nebraska's future will benefit from the information in this atlas: they will learn much about their state and gain insight into future possibilities for even greater productivity in the whole spectrum of agricultural endeavors. The contributors are to be commended for their expert treatment of the great range of subject matter. Special recognition should be given to the project director, Merlin P. Lawson, who provided leadership for the selection of material and the order of presentation. James H. Williams and Doug Murfield, editors, did an excellent job of maintaining a high level of quality in their editing of the writings of the many authors who contributed their expertise to this compendium. Finally, John Magill, cartographic director, deserves a special note of thanks for maintaining a consistent and lucid format for the many illustrations that accompany the text.

This atlas will stand for many years as testimony to the fruitful partnership between the people of the state of Nebraska and their university. As one who labored for nearly four years to strengthen that partnership, I am pleased to note that the *Agricultural Atlas of Nebraska* is at least one indication that the partnership is alive and flourishing.

James H. Zumberge,
Chancellor
University of Nebraska–Lincoln, 1972–75
President
Southern Methodist University, 1975–

PREFACE

One normally considers an atlas to be a collection of maps which cartographically depicts the geographical distributions of the physical, cultural, and economic characteristics of a region. Such reference volumes provide valuable inventories of our natural and human resources as well as exhibiting the geographic diversity of their associations with landform varieties, soil types, vegetative zones, and climatic regions.

The examination and explanation of the interrelationships necessary to an understanding of the total geographical fiber of a region has been seriously omitted from most state atlases until recent years. Decisions required of public officials, bankers and other businessmen, agriculturalists, and involved laymen often necessitate an interpretative form of analysis normally not accompanying the traditional atlas.

Recognizing the merits of providing the public with comprehensive geographical information and analysis, Chancellor James Zumberge, then chancellor of the University of Nebraska–Lincoln, directed the Department of Geography, under the chairmanship of Professor Richard Lonsdale, to establish the Nebraska Atlas Project. The goal of the Project was to provide a geographical inventory of the state of Nebraska by incorporating descriptive maps and graphs with explanatory narrative, a presentation intended to afford the reader some degree of familiarity with the complexity of relationships existing between man and his total environment.

This agricultural volume is the first of a series of topical atlases organized and edited by scholars distinguished in their fields. Each volume represents the coordination of the efforts of many contributors involved in the collection of data, cartography, research, writing, and publication. Future volumes will include a climatological atlas and an economic atlas of Nebraska.

Critical to the success of a continuing project of this nature and magnitude is the cartographic design. In this regard my sincere respect and admiration must be extended to John Magill, who designed and prepared the artwork in his capacity as chief cartographer. The editors of this volume have my heartfelt gratitude for the many hours they expended in organizational and editorial tasks. Their commitment to the project, and the efforts of each contributor, represent an overload on their professional obligations. Without their dedicated efforts this publication could not have been produced.

Finally, without the moral and financial support initiated by Chancellor Zumberge, and the close cooperation among the Institute of Agriculture and National Resources, the Nebraska Department of Agriculture, and the UN–L Department of Geography, this geographical analysis of Nebraska's agriculture would never have been produced. Surely as we plan for the future, a logical prelude to our development is an incisive, comprehensive knowledge of the present.

MERLIN P. LAWSON

INTRODUCTION

Once described as a part of the Great American Desert, Nebraska now has approximately 93 percent of its total land area in farms and ranches. Agriculture is the state's primary source of wealth and its dominant industry. Nebraska ranks sixth in the nation in agricultural income. Today one of every two workers in the state depends directly upon agriculture for employment and many industries involved in all phases of the food and fiber chain from production to marketing are indirectly dependent upon it. Thus, the growth of total income in Nebraska has been closely related to trends in farming.

Nowhere in the nation has the twentieth-century revolution in agriculture taken place more dramatically than in Nebraska. At this time of our nation's bicentennial, it is appropriate to reflect upon the revolutionary changes that have occurred in Nebraska's agriculture and to take cognizance of the importance of its contributions to the state, the nation and, indeed, the world.

This atlas relates the present agricultural situation in Nebraska and the changes that have occurred during the twentieth century, specifically since the 1940s. More than a statistical documentation of the past and present, it represents an effort to trace the development of the various components of the industry and to provide some insight into the causes and effects of agricultural progress.

Written in a nontechnical style, this volume is intended not only for agriculturalists in Nebraska and elsewhere but also for the nonagriculturalist whose general well-being is greatly affected by food and fiber production.

The first chapters describe the natural resources: a climate favorable for the types of farming in Nebraska, abundant water resources, and fertile soils. These are followed by discussions of the development of

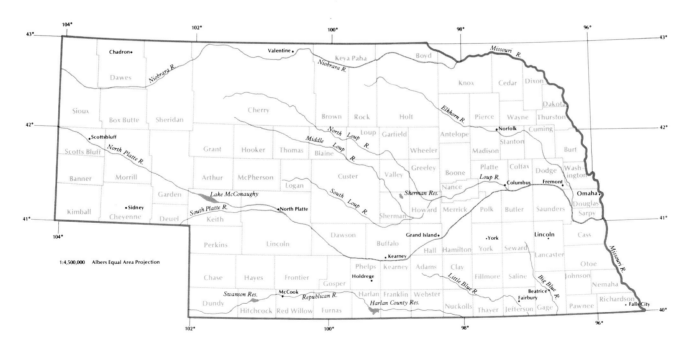

water for agricultural use (Nebraska ranks third in the nation in total irrigated acreage); the continuing efforts and need for preserving and improving the agricultural land base; and the role of mechanization, energy, fertilizers, and pesticides in the new technology.

Nebraska's agriculture is diversified, ranging from corn belt farming in the east to cattle ranching in the Sandhills, Great Plains wheat growing in the west, and irrigation farming in many areas. Thus the chapters on the nature and characteristics of farming and production of crops and livestock form a major portion of the atlas.

Economic considerations of farming and ranching and their impact on the state are presented in the last part. Chapters on marketing include major commodities such as grain and livestock, although marketing of more specialized products such as poultry and horticultural products are included in the discussions of production.

The final chapter summarizes the many factors that influence the course of the state's agriculture and speculates on the changes that may occur in the future.

The primary source of data used in this atlas was the State-Federal Division of Agricultural Statistics. For chapters on types of farming and agricultural economy, the most recent data came from the 1969 *Census of Agriculture*. In a few instances, contributors utilized data from other government agencies or private industry.

Some topics were not specifically covered in the atlas. For example, all crop production data are based on the number of acres harvested. The difference between acres planted and harvested for a crop can vary considerably from year to year. Abandonment of some acres occurs almost every year because of drought, flooding, insect damage, or other causes.

As this nation celebrates its bicentennial, Americans are keenly aware of the tremendous technological innovations that have revolutionized their life-style during its two hundred years of existence. The population has changed from primarily rural to predominantly urban, resulting in an ever increasing burden on the agricultural sector to provide sufficient food for its burgeoning numbers. By necessity, agriculture has evolved into a dynamic, efficient industry of incredible complexity. This volume represents our sincere effort to provide a better understanding of the intricate relationships within the state's most important industry as revealed by Nebraska's spatial and temporal agricultural patterns.

JAMES WILLIAMS
DOUG MURFIELD
MERLIN LAWSON

1
Agricultural Resources

Agroclimatic Resources
Water Resources
Soil Resources

AGROCLIMATIC RESOURCES

Hot summers and cold winters, variability in the distribution of rainfall, fluctuating length of growing season, and frequent winds typify Nebraska's climate, creating uncertainty about the weather and profoundly affecting agricultural production.

Precipitation

Precipitation decreases across the state from an annual average of more than 30 inches in the southeast to less than 15 inches in the west (fig. 1.1). This pattern results from Nebraska's inland location: it is shielded from Pacific Ocean moisture by the coastal and Rocky Mountain ranges; and the western part is more remote than the eastern from the Gulf of Mexico, which provides warm season moisture.

The transitional zone of 18–22 inches of annual precipitation that separates the sub-humid east from the semiarid west shifts back and forth across the state. Omaha in the extreme east has experienced dry years when it received no more precipitation than the average at Scottsbluff in the west; and conversely, western Nebraska has had wet years when it recorded as much precipitation as the norm for Omaha.

About 75 percent of the precipitation falls as rain during the crop-growing months of April through September. Early spring rainfall is generally light, permitting rapid land preparation and planting. Rainfall is heaviest in late May and early June and often delays the harvest of the first cutting of hay. It decreases in July and August, when summer temperatures are highest and crops have the greatest demand for water, so that irrigation is essential for warm-season crops in western Nebraska and often increases yields in the east. Normally, light rainfall and abundant sunshine in the fall favor crop maturation and facilitate harvests.

Growing Season

The length of the growing season, expressed as the number of days when the lowest temperature is above freezing, averages over 170 days in the southeastern part of the state, decreasing to less than 120 days in the extreme northwest (fig. 1.2). Warm-season temperatures, the average dates of the last spring and first fall freezes, and the resulting length of the freeze-free season are

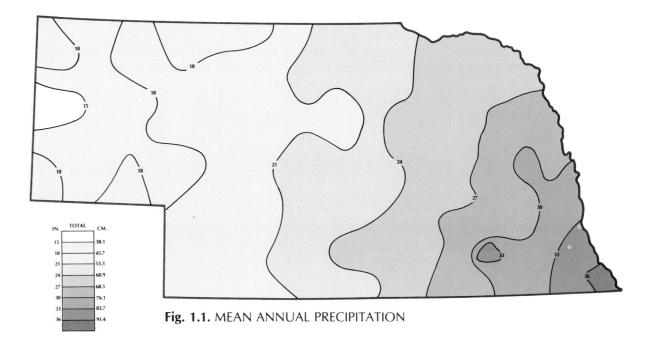

IN.	TOTAL	CM.
15		38.1
18		45.7
21		53.3
24		60.9
27		68.5
30		76.1
33		83.7
36		91.4

Fig. 1.1. MEAN ANNUAL PRECIPITATION

closely related to elevation. The southeast is about 1,000 feet above sea level, while the Panhandle has elevations of 4,000–5,400 feet. There summer temperatures are cooler, the last spring freeze is about four weeks later, the first fall freeze three weeks earlier, and the freeze-free season seven weeks shorter than in the southeast.

The length of the growing season for a specific crop is determined by its response to the entire temperature regime as well as to the average freeze dates. Hardy cool-season crops—small grains, sugar beets, and certain vegetables—continue to grow well even when they are subjected to light spring or fall freezes.

Growing-Degree Days

The time required by different crops and crop varieties to reach maturity is determined to a large extent by the total amount of heat received. Growing-degree days are a measure of the accumulated heat units at any given time during the season and are an indirect measure of crop growth in relation to temperature. They are calculated by subtracting a base temperature of 50°F. from the daily average temperature. (Warm season crops—corn, soybeans, and sorghum—do not grow well below 50°F.)

The number of growing-degree days in Nebraska varies from over 3,000 in the

Agriculture is Nebraska's number 1 industry.

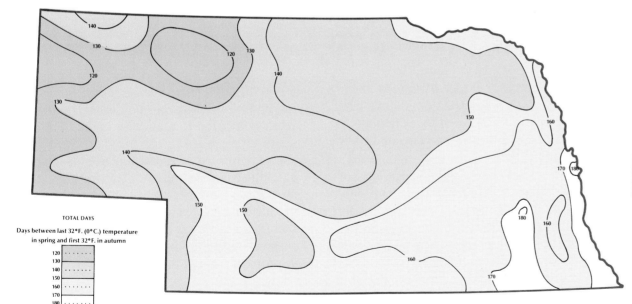

TOTAL DAYS

Days between last 32°F. (0°C.) temperature in spring and first 32°F. in autumn

120	. . . . . .
130	
140	. . . . . .
150	
160	. . . . .
170	
180	. . . . . .

Fig. 1.2. MEAN ANNUAL FREEZE-FREE SEASON

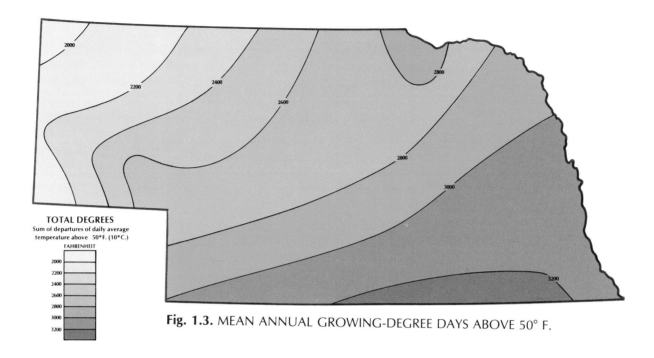

Fig. 1.3. MEAN ANNUAL GROWING-DEGREE DAYS ABOVE 50° F.

southeast to less than 2,000 in the northwest (fig. 1.3). Short-season hybrids requiring fewer growing-degree days to mature are the only type of corn adapted to the western part of the state, and they may be harvested for silage instead of grain in years when temperatures are below normal and the number of growing-degree days less than average. Hybrids adapted to warmer regions may require 3,000 or more growing-degree days.

Livestock Stress

Livestock stress occurs when the temper-ature rises above 80°F. for prolonged peri-ods, particularly when the humidity is high and the cattle are confined for fattening. These conditions result in an elevated body temperature, higher respiration rate, faster than normal heartbeat, and consequent low-er feed efficiency in meat animals and milk-producing dairy cattle.

The average number of days in the sum-mer when the temperature is 80°F. or higher decreases from over 110 in the south to less than 70 in the northwest (fig. 1.4). The num-ber of hours per day with temperatures above 80° F. shows a similar distribution pattern: during late July, the hottest time of the year, the temperature is above 80° F. less than four hours per day in the north-west, compared to about ten hours in the south.

Late-winter storms, particularly during the calving season in March, can also be haz-ardous to livestock. Strong winds with blow-ing, drifting snow cause cattle to scatter and complicate feeding operations; and wet snow or cold rain and wind may fatally chill unprotected newborn calves.

4

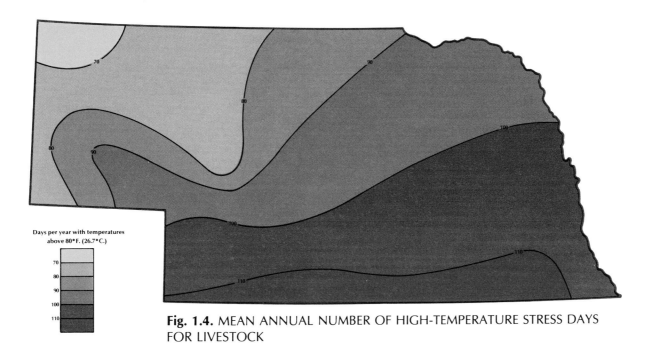

Days per year with temperatures
above 80° F. (26.7° C.)

70
80
90
100
110

Fig. 1.4. MEAN ANNUAL NUMBER OF HIGH-TEMPERATURE STRESS DAYS FOR LIVESTOCK

Adaptations to the Weather

Agriculture will undoubtedly always be affected by the vagaries of weather, but new crop varieties and farming procedures are constantly being developed to minimize adverse effects of the climate.

Irrigation, currently at more than 5 million acres in the state, provides a buffer against drought, a serious recurrent problem for the Great Plains. It stabilizes yield and is conducive to crop diversification. For example, during the drought of 1974, irrigated corn yielded ninety-three bushels per acre, compared to twenty-six bushels for dryland fields that were not abandoned.

The careful selection of crops and planting times and the use of strip cropping, stubble mulching, deferred grazing, and other such practices have also enabled Nebraska farmers to cope with weather uncertainty. Sugar beets, an important crop in the Panhandle, tolerate untimely late spring or early fall frost and have a remarkable ability to recover from hail. Irrigated field beans, susceptible to diseases in more humid areas, benefit from the drier summers in the west and mature early enough to escape damage from fall frost even though planted in June. Grain sorghum is tolerant to heat and drought and has become the major dryland crop in the south-central and southeastern areas of the state. Winter wheat is well adapted because its major growth occurs during the cooler and wetter spring months.

RALPH NEILD

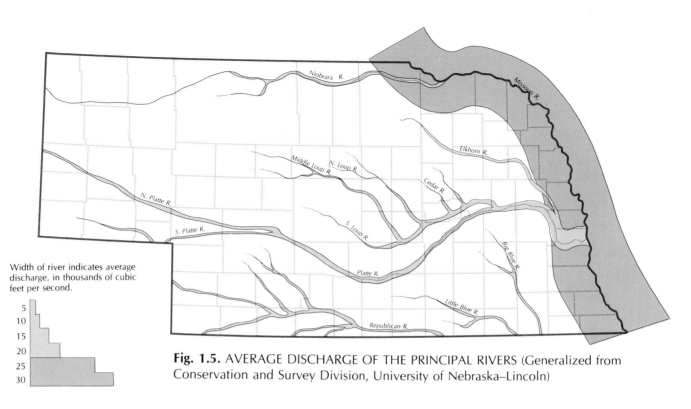

Width of river indicates average discharge, in thousands of cubic feet per second.

5
10
15
20
25
30

Fig. 1.5. AVERAGE DISCHARGE OF THE PRINCIPAL RIVERS (Generalized from Conservation and Survey Division, University of Nebraska–Lincoln)

WATER RESOURCES

Nebraska is a water-rich state. Underneath 59 percent of its land surface, in porous rock beds called aquifers, is stored nearly 2 billion acre-feet of good-quality groundwater, most of which is easily accessible. Added to that, from 1965 to 1975 there was an annual precipitation ranging from 59 to 126 million acre-feet, averaging 90 million acre-feet, and an annual surface-water inflow of roughly 2 million acre-feet. Since approximately 8 million acre-feet flows out of the state, at least 6 million acre-feet of surface-water flow is generated within the state annually.

Precipitation

Precipitation is an important source of Nebraska's water supply, averaging, for the period 1931–73, 21.9 inches—almost 30 trillion gallons of water, or about 385 million gallons per square mile, or 80,000 cubic feet per acre—a year. (For a full discussion of precipitation in Nebraska, see the preceding section, "Agroclimatic Resources.")

Surface Water

The amount of surface water in Nebraska is not large in comparison to either the enormous quantities of groundwater in the state or the amount of surface water in eastern states that have a higher annual precipitation. The streams are not deep and the numerous lakes are for the most part small and shallow. However, the quality of the surface water, like that of the groundwater, is generally good to excellent.

Surface water in Nebraska drains generally eastward from the higher elevations in the western part of the state (fig. 1.5). Eventually all the surface water flowing in the state reaches the Missouri River, draining either directly into it through such rivers as the Platte, Niobrara, and Nemaha or indirectly through rivers such as the Little Blue, the Big Blue, and the Republican into the Kan-

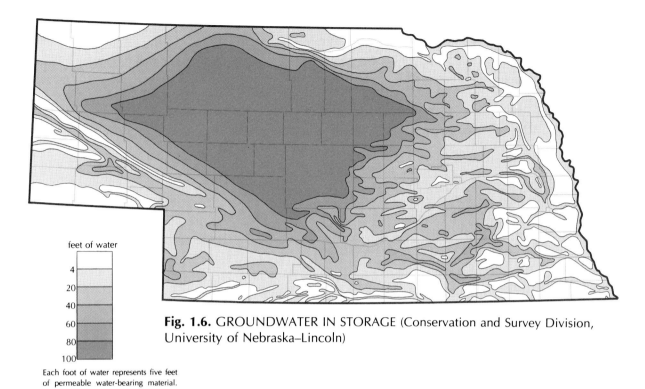

feet of water

4	
20	
40	
60	
80	
100	

Each foot of water represents five feet
of permeable water-bearing material.

Fig. 1.6. GROUNDWATER IN STORAGE (Conservation and Survey Division,
University of Nebraska–Lincoln)

sas River, which in turn empties into the Missouri. In terms of surface water, Nebraska is a donor, passing on to other states approximately 6 million acre-feet more water than flows into its borders.

Groundwater

The entire central and west-central part of the state is underlain by an enormous reservoir of groundwater centering in the Sandhills, where porous sands inhibit surface runoff and allow great quantities of water to percolate down to the aquifers of sand, sandstone, and gravel (fig. 1.6).

Large or moderate quantities of ground-water are available for wells over more than 80 percent of Nebraska. Wells supplying more than 300 gallons per minute (gpm) can be obtained in more than half the state, and irrigation wells yielding over 500 gpm and upward to 2,500 gpm can be obtained in many places.

The amount of groundwater fluctuates slightly depending on the wetness or dryness of the particular year, but the wet years tend to balance out the dry years, so that groundwater supplies stay nearly the same over extended periods of time.

Irrigation

Nebraska ranks among the top three irrigation states of the nation, with approximately 5 million acres under irrigation. Surface-water irrigation, the earliest form in the state, began soon after the Civil War, although its major development dates from about 1890. Today Nebraska has 1 million acres under surface-water irrigation.

Groundwater irrigation began in the 1920s and, with the development of drilling techniques and deep-well turbines, became the dominant form. At the beginning of 1975 nearly 44,500 registered irrigation wells supplied groundwater to 4 million

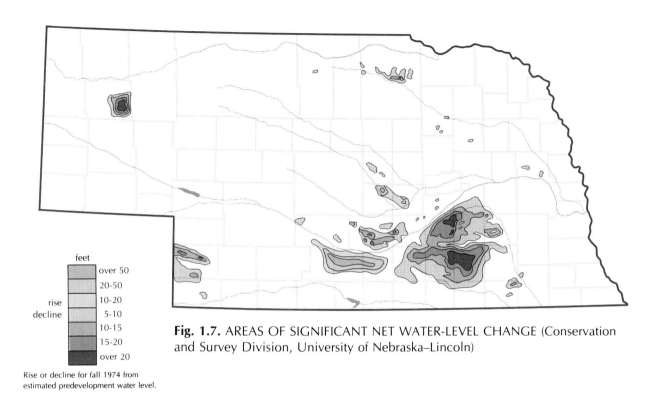

feet

	over 50
	20-50
rise	10-20
decline	5-10
	10-15
	15-20
	over 20

Rise or decline for fall 1974 from
estimated predevelopment water level.

Fig. 1.7. AREAS OF SIGNIFICANT NET WATER-LEVEL CHANGE (Conservation and Survey Division, University of Nebraska–Lincoln)

acres, for an average of approximately 89 acres per well.

Water Use

Nebraska's water use in 1970 totaled 14.8 billion gallons per day. Of that amount, roughly 13.6 billion gallons, or 92 percent, was used for irrigation. All other uses—municipal, industrial, and rural—account for only about 8 percent. The per capita water use averages approximately 4,000 gallons per day, twice the national average.

Although Nebraska has an abundant wa-ter supply, the question of how much longer water use can continue to increase on a statewide basis is far from rhetorical. The vast supply of good-quality water is not evenly distributed across the state. Some areas have more water than is being used; others have mined their groundwater so vigorously that the dwindling of reserves has become a pressing concern (fig. 1.7). Since continued irrigation is essential to Nebraska's agricultural economy, good manage-ment of the state's water resources is needed if irrigation development is to pro-ceed without bringing calamitous results to certain regions.

Sound water management will require planning for more storage in on-stream and off-stream reservoirs, for more storage dur-ing wet years, and for additional storage of water that finally enters the groundwater supply. It will also necessitate planned re-charge through the use of canals, wells, and pits, and may require the integration of surface water and groundwater for irrigation purposes. The optimum use of Nebraska's water resources will also mean that the

8

individual user will have to conserve water, use it more efficiently, restrict his water use where possible, adopt new soil moisture–saving practices where feasible, and in all cases manage carefully the water resources that are becoming increasingly more valuable.

VINCE DREESZEN
JAY FUSSELL

SOIL RESOURCES

Origin of Soil Properties

The soils of Nebraska are a product of the action of climate and biological organisms on the parent materials as modified by local topography, drainage, and the length of time the materials have been exposed to weathering.

Two types of geologic deposits are parent materials for the vast majority of soils in the state. Throughout the eastern, southern, southwestern and Panhandle areas, most of the soils have formed in wind-blown silt and clay, or loess. Wind-blown sand is the parent material in the Sandhills region that occupies a vast area in the north-central part of the state. Within the valleys of major streams, soils have formed in alluvium of recent origin. While these soils are not extensive in terms of acreage, they are among the most productive in terms of crop yields. Old glacial till and loess are parent

materials for soils on lower parts of the landscape in the southeastern region. Here a thinner loess cap exists and erosion has removed it from side slopes, exposing older materials beneath. Soils have formed in residuum from shale and sandstone in local areas in the Panhandle and northern part of the state, while other soils in the northern area have formed in outwash sands and gravels, partly reworked by wind.

Climate and biological organisms, mainly vegetation, must be considered together when examining their impact on soil formation because vegetation is very dependent on the climate. It appears that soils in Nebraska have formed under a grassy type of vegetation associated with a semiarid or subhumid climate similar to that of today.

All of the state's soils are young geologically. Those in the stream valleys are so young that their soil profiles are not well developed. Their relatively young age, combined with factors of climate and vegetation, means that they are not highly leached, but contain most of the elements that were present in the parent materials. Calcium, magnesium, potassium, and phosphorus are abundant in most of the soils of the state, and all but those in the southeast have lime zones beneath their profiles, indicating that leaching has not been severe. This condition leads to fertile soils that are very productive if water can be made available through irrigation and if good farming practices are used.

Topography and subsequent soil drainage have greatly influenced the development of soil properties in local areas. For example,

throughout the Crete-Hastings and the Holdrege-Colby Associations (nos. 26 and 23 in figure 1.8), there are surface depressions of from less than one to several acres which pond water that runs from surrounding land. Soils in these basins are poorly drained and have thick, dense claypans as subsoils, while surrounding soils lack the claypan and are better drained.

Nebraska Soils as Resources for Agriculture

When a soil-association map (fig. 1.8) and a land-use map (fig. 1.9) of Nebraska are compared, it is apparent that row crop and forage production is primarily on loessal soils and in the stream valleys, while nearly all rangeland is on soils formed in aeolian (wind-blown) sand. There are good reasons for this distribution. The soils formed in loess are composed almost wholly of silt and clay. They are able to retain a large amount of water for plant use and to hold essential plant nutrients well. The clay fraction of these soils contains significant amounts of expanding-lattice clay minerals that have a high cation exchange capacity and hold basic ions such as calcium, magnesium, sodium, potassium, and ammonium in the soil against leaching. Moreover, leaching of soluble anions such as nitrate from these fine-textured soils is not rapid under Nebraska's climate, unless excessive irrigation water is applied. The loess in which these soils formed contains appreciable amounts of feldspars, micas, amphibole, pyroxenes, and apatite, which on weathering, release essential plant nutrients into

1 Pierre–Samsil
2 Bridgeport–Keith
3 Rough broken land
4 Keith–Rosebud
5 Anselmo–Keith
6 Mitchell–Tripp
7 Valentine–Dunday
8 McCook–Las
9 Keith–Colby
10 Holt–Valentine
11 Reliance–Boyd
12 Thurman–Jansen
13 Loup–Valentine
14 Thurman–Valentine
15 Moody–Crofton
16 Crofton–Nora

17 Colby–Ulysses
18 Hall–Wood River
19 Leshara–Platte
20 Sharpsburg–Marshall
21 Marshall–Monona
22 Luton–Haynie
23 Holdrege–Colby
24 Holdrege–Hastings
25 Kenesaw–Holdrege
26 Hastings–Crete
27 Sharpsburg–Shelby
28 Crete–Fillmore
29 Crete–Wymore
30 Wymore–Pawnee
31 Lancaster–Hedville

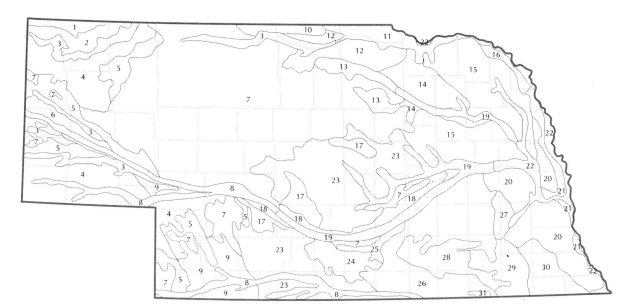

Fig. 1.8. SOIL ASSOCIATIONS (Conservation and Survey Division, University of Nebraska–Lincoln)

the soil. The availability of nutrients, coupled with the organic matter formed many hundreds of years under grass vegetation, has given these soils a great capacity to produce if water is available. Although the soils in most parts of the state contain a high level of natural fertility, supplemental nitrogen fertilizer must be supplied to obtain the high yields that farmers commonly aim for. Since most nitrogen sources cause soils to become more acid, lime is also needed on some soils in the eastern part of the state which are slightly acid under normal conditions.

Because the majority of the alluvium in the stream valleys was derived from loess, these soils also are extremely productive. Many bottom-land soils are subirrigated or are near a source of water for surface irrigation. Hence, the stream valleys and terraces are some of the most productive areas in the state. For example, the average yields of irrigated corn on a Hord soil on a stream terrace and a Hobbs soil on stream flood plains in Seward County are around 150 bushels per acre, the highest for irrigated corn in the county. Dryland yields of corn on these two soils are nearly 90 bushels per

acre. In contrast, the Pawnee soil formed in glacial till averaged only 60 bushels per acre.

Many of the weatherable minerals that release nutrients essential for plant growth are also found in the aeolian sands of the Sandhills, but the droughty nature of the sandy soils has led to sparser grass cover and a lower organic matter content than in the finer-textured soils. That plus the lack of fine particles to hold water and nutrients, and the fact that the sands blow badly when exposed to the wind, has restricted land use there to rangeland. However, the area is

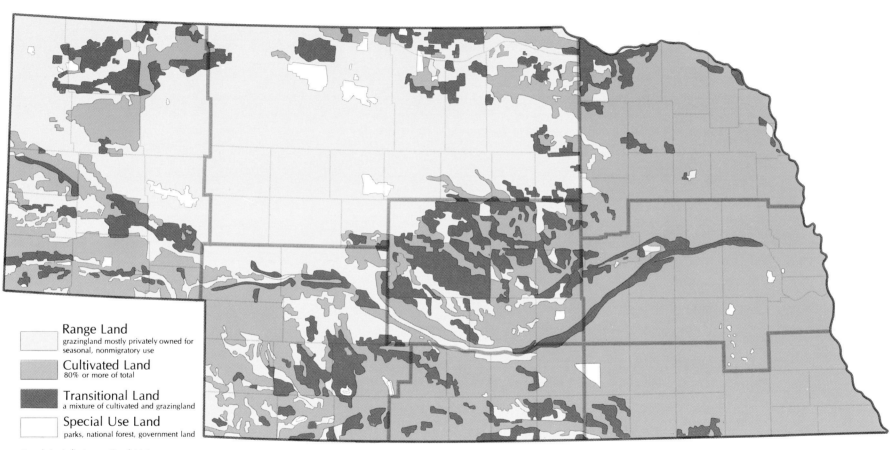

Range Land
grazingland mostly privately owned for seasonal, nonmigratory use

Cultivated Land
80% or more of total

Transitional Land
a mixture of cultivated and grazingland

Special Use Land
parks, national forest, government land

Boundaries indicate reporting districts.

Fig. 1.9. LAND-USE STRATIFICATION (Nebraska State–Federal Division of Agricultural Statistics)

excellent rangeland. The many subirrigated valleys provide a large amount of forage from natural and introduced grasses. The moisture-holding capacity of the sands is sufficient to bring about good growth of cool-season grasses on the spring range.

The Sandhills has beneath it the largest reserve of subsurface water in the state. With the introduction of center-pivot irrigation systems has come the development of land in the Sandhills for irrigated crops. In some of the valleys where the soils do not slope steeply, crops can be produced under good water, land, and fertilizer management. In other places, mismanagement or the ill-advised location of irrigation systems has created bare, sandy areas where wind erosion has become severe. In most of the Sandhills region the soils are too sloping for successful sprinkler irrigation. Because the soft, sandy nature of the soils makes them difficult to irrigate and to stabilize with vegetation when the topography is modified through leveling, it is probable that the Sandhills will remain primarily rangeland.

DAVE LEWIS

12

2
Resource Development and Improvement

Irrigation
Soil and Water Resources Conservation
Farm Supplies

IRRIGATION

The Irrigated Acreage

With 5,400,000 acres under irrigation in 1975, Nebraska was the third-ranking irrigation state, following California, which had an estimated 8,759,000 acres, and Texas, which had some 8,500,000 acres. During the five-year period 1970–75, Nebraska had the greatest increase in irrigated acreage of any state—a total of 1,402,000 acres, for an average of 280,400 acres per year (fig. 2.1) and a rate of increase ranging from 5.1 to 6.9 percent per year, four times the rate in either California or Texas. Moreover, when the availability of land and water (both surface water and groundwater) in the leading agricultural states is compared, Nebraska appears to have greater potential than other states for the continued expanson of its irrigated acreage. Approximately 40 percent of the total land in Nebraska, 19.2 million acres, has soils that are suitable for irrigation.

Early Irrigation in Nebraska

Irrigation has had a place in Nebraska's agriculture since the territorial period. In 1859 an irrigation ditch was constructed on the South Platte River near the present site of North Platte, and seven years later a small irrigation system was built near Fort McPherson on the Platte River, also in present Lincoln County.

In 1871, a second irrigation ditch was built on the South Platte River, but the Bay State Canal, now known as the Bickel Canal, on Little Lodgepole Creek in Kimball County, has the first priority of record (December 31, 1876) to surface water flows in Nebraska. The first sizable irrigation enterprise in the state was the North Platte Canal, in Lincoln County, built in 1883 and 1884. Between that time and 1895, several canals were built in the Platte, Frenchman, Republican, and Niobrara valleys. The present Mirage Flats project in Sheridan County even follows the canal alignment of an early attempt to irrigate the Niobrara valley.

During the 1880s, water rights were filed on most of the flowing streams and rivers in the western part of the state, especially the North Platte and Platte Rivers. The period 1891–94 also saw the construction of many more irrigation ditches throughout the western part of the state.

The extremely dry years following 1892 heightened interest in irrigation as settlers realized its vital role in crop production. An irrigation district law passed in 1895 permitted the refinancing of many of the existing older systems and the organization of new irrigation districts.

The drought of the 1930s hastened the development of numerous surface-water irri-

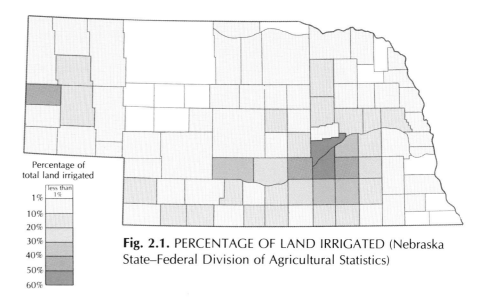

Percentage of
total land irrigated

	less than 1%
1%	
10%	
20%	
30%	
40%	
50%	
60%	

Fig. 2.1. PERCENTAGE OF LAND IRRIGATED (Nebraska State–Federal Division of Agricultural Statistics)

14

gation projects and irrigation wells, especially on the river valleys where static water levels were close to the surface, and prompted the funding of water-storage and irrigation projects that had been proposed as early as the turn of the century.

The Development of Well and Pump Irrigation

Early irrigation wells were generally dug or drilled in river valleys where water tables were close to the surface and lifts were shallow, enabling centrifugal pumps to operate efficiently. Before irrigation on the plains above the valleys became a practical reality, the development of pumps, engines, water-distribution methods, and well-drilling equipment and techniques was required. In 1903 a well driller adapted the rotary type of drilling rig used in the oil fields to the drilling of deeper irrigation wells and built a deep-well "pitless" pump, the antecedent of what is now called the turbine pump.

The final problem to overcome before pump irrigation could become practical was the development of a dependable and cheap power supply. By 1910 electric motors and electricity powered some irrigation pumps, but electric-generating capacity was limited and distribution was restricted. In the late 1890s low-compression oil-burning engines were first used to power irrigation pumps in the Great Plains. The widespread interest in the internal-combustion gasoline engine led to the adaptation of the Otto four-cycle internal-combustion engine, and later came the adaptation of natural gas

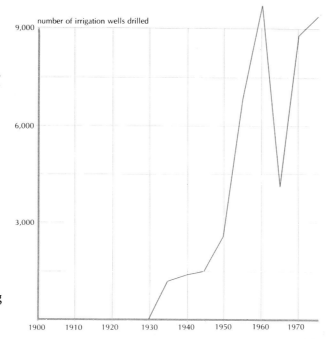

Graph 2.1. IRRIGATION WELLS DRILLED, 1900–1975 (Nebraska Natural Resources Commission)

and diesel engines to power turbine pumps and the use of propane or L.P.-fueled engines.

Irrigation wells became common in Nebraska in the 1930s. While there undoubtedly were earlier irrigation wells dug by hand or drilled, the first that are currently registered were three wells installed between 1921 and 1930. Five more were drilled from 1931 to 1935; then 1935 marked a boom year: 1,195 new irrigation wells were installed as the need created by the severe drought coincided with the availability of the necessary technology. The number of wells installed from 1971

through March 31, 1975—9,334—almost equals the five-year high, 9,719, recorded for 1956–60 (graph 2.1).

Surface and Groundwater Irrigation

As of January 1, 1975, about 1,108,000 acres, or about one of every five acres under irrigation, used surface-water sources (fig. 2.2). The remaining irrigated acreage depended upon groundwater supplied by nearly 44,500 registered irrigation wells (fig. 2.3).

The last major surface-water irrigation project constructed in Nebraska, the Ainsworth project, completed in 1965, delivers water to nearly 34,000 acres. Since 1965, when 2,914,000 acres were under irrigation, an additional 2,486,000 acres have been irrigated, at least 98 percent of that total as a result of the installation of irrigation wells.

The ideal arrangement for irrigation is to use both surface- and groundwater supplies. This is best illustrated by the tri-county area of Gosper, Phelps, and Kearney Counties, where 2,709 irrigation wells serve an estimated 256,200 acres, while another 115,000 acres are irrigated by a network of reservoirs and canals. This conjunctive use has substantially increased groundwater supplies since the project first began operation in 1942.

Sprinkler Irrigation

Without question, the rapid increase in irrigation in Nebraska since 1965 has been due to widespread use of sprinkler irriga-

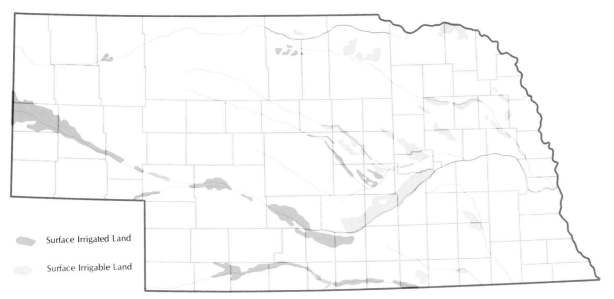

Surface Irrigated Land

Surface Irrigable Land

Fig. 2.2. EXISTING AND POTENTIAL AREAS OF SURFACE IRRIGATION (U.S. Department of the Interior)

tion. It was introduced after World War II using, first, hand-moved sprinkler lines, then towlines, wheel-move or side-roll sprinkler systems, and boom sprinklers. Recently, the most popular form has been the center-pivot self-propelled sprinkler system, a revolutionary invention of great consequence to the state's agriculture. Center-pivot irrigation systems made it possible to irrigate sandy-profile soils of uneven topography not suited to the gravity type of irrigation. They eliminated most of the labor required with other types of sprinkler irrigation equipment and opened millions of acres of relatively low-

cost land to irrigation development.

In the late 1960s and early 1970s, center-pivot irrigation began to account for more and more of the increase in irrigated acreage in Nebraska. In 1965, only 14 such systems were operating in the nine southwestern counties. By December 31, 1969, there were 349; and data from the ERTS-1 satellite collected in July and August 1974 revealed more than 1,100 in that area.

The cost of a complete center-pivot irrigation system for 160 acres, with 133 acres irrigated, rose from an average of $26,256 in 1969 to an estimated $60,000 in 1975.

Despite the cost, however, center-pivot is by far the fastest-growing method of irrigation in the state, accounting for an estimated 60–70 percent of the 267,000-acre increase in irrigated land from 1973 to 1974. In addition, many farmers who were using other types of irrigation systems have converted to center-pivot because of its labor-saving features and other advantages.

The Results of Irrigation

Irrigation has greatly lessened the effects of drought and helped stabilize crop production. Its advantages vary from year to year, depending on the amount and frequency of rainfall in different areas of the state. For example, in 1972, when rainfall was above normal, nonirrigated corn averaged 85.4 bushels per acre and irrigated corn 124.1 bushels. But in 1974, a year that was extremely dry across the state, nonirrigated crop yields were reduced substantially and in many cases crops intended for grain were either cut for silage or abandoned.

Table 2.1 shows the 1974 yields of principal irrigated and nonirrigated crops in Nebraska, and also illustrates the effects of irrigation.

Subirrigated Lands

In addition to the 5,400,000 irrigated acreage in the state, several hundred thousand acres of subirrigated land exist in the river valleys and the wet meadow areas of the Sandhills. While this type of land is not

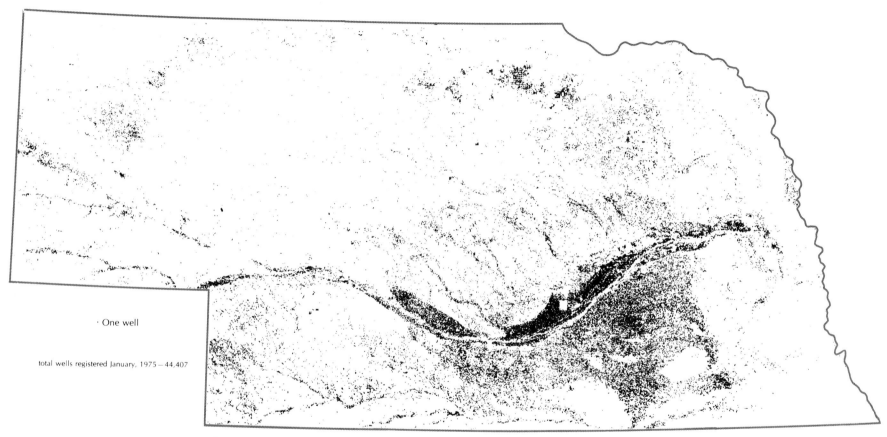

· One well

total wells registered January, 1975 — 44,407

Fig. 2.3. REGISTERED IRRIGATION WELLS (Conservation and Survey Division, University of Nebraska–Lincoln)

Table 2.1. Principal Irrigated and Nonirrigated Crops, 1974

Crop	Harvested Acres			Average Yield per Acre	
	Irr. (1000)	Nonirr. (1000)	Irr. (%)	Irr.	Nonirr.
Corn for grain	3,050	2,550	54.5	103.0 bu	26.1 bu
Corn for silage	300	670	30.9	NA	NA
Alfalfa hay	299	1,441	17.2	3.2 tons	2.29 tons
Sorghum for grain	170	1,780	8.7	55 bu	30.9 bu
Dry edible beans	113	———	100.0	1,950 lb.	———
Soybeans	103	1,087	8.7	32.7 bu	23.2 bu
Sugar beets	76	———	100.0	18.1 tons	———
Wheat	30	2,870	1.0	48.4 bu	34.0 bu
Totals	4,141	10,398	28.5		

NA = Not available.

irrigated in a traditional sense, the existence of a high water table provides crops such as alfalfa or native stands of grass with water for excellent production. Much of the alfalfa acreage in river valleys like those in Dawson County and the highly productive haylands in the wet meadow areas in Holt, Brown, Rock, and Cherry Counties are subirrigated.

The Economic Impact of Irrigation

The impact of irrigation on Nebraska's economy is tremendous, amounting in 1963, for example, to $302.32 per acre. In addition, the direct investment impact, when nonirrigated land was converted to irrigated land, amounted to an estimated $712 per acre. For 1970, the total impact for each acre irrigated—that is, the value of the increased production due to irrigation—amounted to $499.77. Multiplying this figure by the number of acres irrigated in 1970, 3,998,000, the total economic impact amounted to nearly $2 billion. While the level farm costs rose very rapidly between 1970 and 1974, the level of prices for most farm commodities, especially grains, rose even more rapidly. Multiplying the 1970 figure of $499.77 by the number of acres irrigated in 1975, 5,400,000, without any upward correction for farm commodity price changes, the total economic impact amounted to an impressive estimate of $2.7 billion.

LESLIE F. SHEFFIELD

Deep loess soil, typical of rolling land in eastern Nebraska.

SOIL AND WATER RESOURCES CONSERVATION

The moldboard plow stands next to the rifle and six gun in its reputation for having won the west. The best farmer in the early days was the man who plowed the straightest furrows and achieved the cleanest field by turning under all crop residue. Over the years, experience has shown that those methods failed to protect the soil for long-term productivity.

In the 1930s, pioneer agricultural environmentalists began efforts to control wind and water erosion on land where overgrazing and cultivation had destroyed protective vegetation. Extensive shelterbelts were planted. Aided by the Soil Conservation Service, farmers and ranchers experimented with methods, often crude by today's standards, to hold the topsoil against wind and to keep rainfall from washing gullies across their land.

Nebraska excels in taking the initiative to solve its conservation problems and is unique in having twenty-four Natural Resources Districts that exercise broad authority, including levying local taxes used to encourage proper development of both soil and water resources (fig. 2.4). The establishment of a state Resources Development Fund also shows the importance Nebraska places upon soil and water resources.

Today new methods of utilizing soil resources are being adopted by Nebraska farmers and ranchers. The majority no longer plow straight furrows up and downhill; even gently rolling land is farmed along contours. Plowing is being replaced by various forms of reduced tillage which maintain crop residue to protect vulnerable soil against both wind and water. The scheduled rotation of livestock reduces overgrazing and utilizes fragile natural rangeland and pastures to the best advantage without destroying surface cover. The improvement of rangeland by controlling weeds and balancing warm- and cool-season grasses evens out grazing pressure on the land.

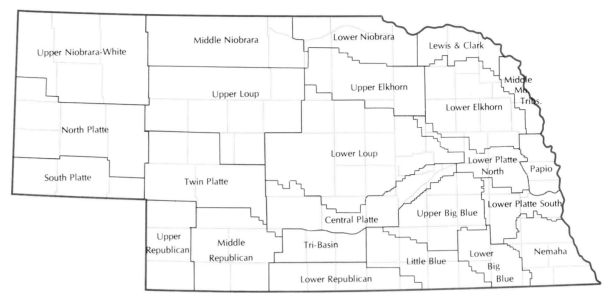

Fig. 2.4. NATURAL RESOURCE DISTRICTS (Nebraska Natural Resources Commission)

The Effects of Climate and Topography

Natural cover, crops, and cropping practices vary widely across the state and are dependent on rainfall, sunshine, humidity, topography, and type of soil. Both the amount of erosion that occurs and conservation practices are closely interrelated with these factors.

The western two-thirds of Nebraska lies in the Great Plains region typified by low rainfall, low humidity, and generally unobstructed winds, all contributing to potentially serious erosion problems. Rainfall varies considerably in amount, distribution, and intensity from year to year in all areas, causing droughts and wet years, each with special conservation problems due to poor surface cover or intense runoff.

The topography consists of gently rolling land broken by isolated buttes, mesas, and ravines. Because of the gradual rise in elevation from east to west, Nebraska has in its thirteen river basins many shallow rivers and streams flowing generally eastward.

Some erosion occurs naturally. In Nebraska a general allowable limit is 4–5 tons of soil loss per acre per year, about 1/45 inch thickness over the entire surface. This limit is based upon the tendency for freezing and thawing, wetting and drying, and plant and animal activities to break down subsoil into topsoil. The amount of natural erosion which would occur, given the original plant cover before cultivation, is also considered in calculating it.

Conservation Problems

In spite of progress in the struggle to preserve soil and water—the two most important natural resources in this predominantly agricultural state—much remains to be accomplished. Sediment is the worst pollutant (by volume) of the surface waters and, deposited in drainage ways, dams, roads, streets, and yards, costs millions of dollars in damage and waste each year. Runoff causes chemical pollution as it carries phosphates, which are attached to the sediment, and soluble nitrates into surface water.

At least 36 million acres—75 percent of the state's land—is threatened by erosion, 19 million primarily by water and 17 million by wind erosion (graph 2.2). Of those 36 million acres, 14 million are cropland, with 25 percent protected, and 21 million are pasture and rangeland, with 45 percent adequately protected. In all, only 13.5 million acres are adequately protected, leaving 23 million acres needing at least some treatment.

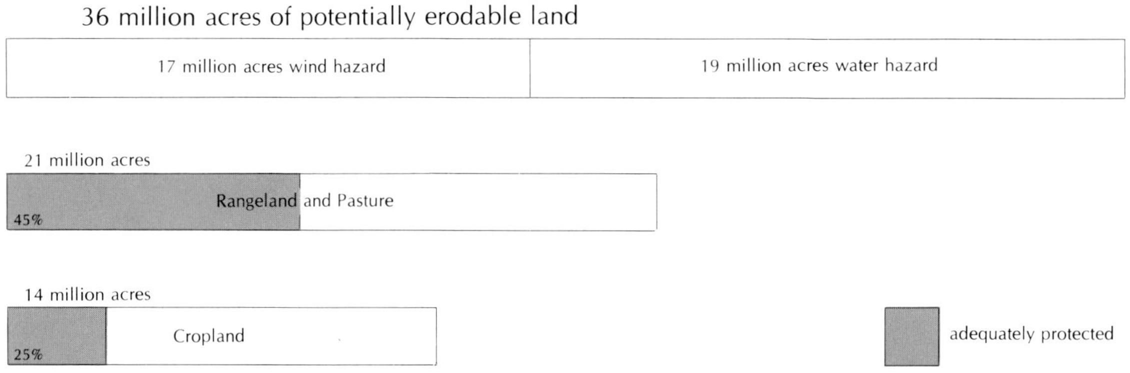

Wind Erosion

Wind erosion is a potentially serious threat for at least 9 million acres—nearly 2 million of cropland and 7 million of rangeland and pasture—of the 17 million acres primarily subject to its damage. Although 70 percent of the 17 million acres is located in the

36 million acres of potentially erodable land

| 17 million acres wind hazard | 19 million acres water hazard |

21 million acres

Rangeland and Pasture
45%

14 million acres

Cropland
25%

adequately protected

Graph 2.2. WIND AND WATER EROSION

Sandhills, wind erosion is not unique to that area. Nebraska's unique Sandhills has 20,000 square miles of sand dunes held in place by native grasses. Disruption of this cover by concentration of livestock or by cultivation must be carefully managed in order to keep the loose, sandy soil in place; otherwise, a blowout occurs and the bare soil becomes more vulnerable to wind erosion.

In nonirrigated western areas, some cropland is allowed to lie fallow for a season to accumulate soil moisture for the next year's grain crop. Management of surface residue by stubble mulching and planned grazing is effective in protecting soil from both wind and water. Shelterbelts, occupying 160,000 acres, and strip cropping, practiced on nearly 2.4 million acres, reduce the force of the

wind. They, along with emergency tillage practices, are most effective when oriented at right angles to the wind.

Water Erosion

Of the 19 million acres on which water erosion is the major threat, 14 million, or 30 percent of the state's area, still need treatment.

Rolling hills predominate in eastern Nebraska, where wind-blown silt or clay soil, called loess, rests on undulating glacial deposits. Rainfall can be very intense in these eastern hills, causing various erosion problems. In the northeast, topsoil is generally deep, and moderate to severe erosion causes only minor crop-production difficulties. The more noticeable signs of erosion such as gullies are seldom found. This area

20

is, however, the source of large amounts of sediment resulting from sheet erosion. In the southeast, topsoil is generally thin and even slight erosion causes severe damage and production problems. Water-storage facilities are often unable to cope with heavy amounts of runoff, and flooding, erosion, and sedimentation occur. Conservation practices such as terracing, crop residue management, contour farming, and wise pasture management reduce runoff and hold water on the land.

Gully erosion is a serious problem in many areas of Nebraska. In the Nemaha Basin and the Missouri tributaries as much as 5–8 percent of the land will be affected, should the present gully erosion go unchecked.

Sheet and rill erosion have caused permanent loss of productivity in the glacial till areas of the Lower Platte, Big Blue, and Nemaha River Basins. Some areas in the loess hills of the Missouri tributaries and the Elkhorn and Lower Platte River Basins have lost six inches or more of topsoil by erosion in the last fifty years.

Irrigation Conservation Problems

About 19 million acres, mainly in central and western Nebraska, are considered suitable for irrigation. Under good water management, 7 million acres would have few soil conservation problems even with intensive irrigation; 4 million acres would incur moderate conservation problems; and the other 8 million acres would either have severe physical limitations or would be un-

suitable without major land-improvement measures such as flood control or drainage.

Technological advances and economic changes may overcome some of the present restrictions. However, application of new technology requires careful assessment of each situation. In the Sandhills severe erosion has occurred on abandoned pivot-irrigation fields that were reshaped so that pivots could function and later were discovered to be unsuited for irrigation.

Irrigated lands often have special soil and water conservation problems. Overwatering may result in excessive runoff, and land irrigated by pivot systems sometimes incur erosion resulting from water runoff in wheel tracks. The removal of shelterbelts for irrigation development has drawn the attention of conservationists, who fear a recurrence of the "dirty thirties." The removal of terraces to make travel easier for pivot systems increases the hazards of water erosion.

Erosion Control

Nebraska's agricultural practices need not accelerate natural erosion. Water-borne soil movement is caused primarily by farming up and down slopes with minimum surface cover. These soil losses can be reduced or avoided by a number of means.

Contour farming—farming across the slopes—prevents rainfall runoff from flowing directly downhill and can effect up to a 50 percent reduction in erosion. Water is trapped by furrows and ridges, increasing infiltration and reducing its erosive capability. The number of acres on which con-

tour farming is practiced increased from 170,000 in 1955 to more than 4 million in 1975.

Terraces, which can also reduce water erosion up to 50 percent, perform much the same function. They are larger permanent ridges of earth with a channel on the uphill side to collect runoff and safely conduct it from the field. Between 1955 and 1975, terraces in Nebraska increased from 8,000 miles to 167,000 miles, on more than 3.5 million acres. Outdated contour terrace systems have become objectionable, because of the irregular spacing between terraces, to many farmers who use large equipment. Some farmers are removing old terraces, leaving the land unprotected. Where parallel terrace systems are used, irregular spacing problems are minimized. These terraces are evenly spaced on the basis of a multiple of the width of the farmer's equipment and slope of the land. Since the mid-1960s, when they were first used in Nebraska, 2,500 miles of parallel terraces had been built by 1975. A 75 percent reduction in erosion can be achieved by the use of terraces in conjunction with contour farming.

Of all field erosion control methods, tillage practices offer the greatest potential, affording up to a 90 percent reduction in erosion. The ideal of the clean field dies slowly, but the most practical and immediate method of controlling erosion is to maintain sufficient plant residue. Excessive tillage buries crop residue and dries out the soil. The majority of Nebraska's farmers practice some form of reduced tillage. In combination with contour farming and terracing, it can prevent up to 98 percent of erosion.

Water Conservation

Water conservation is closely akin to soil conservation. The most effective methods of soil conservation reduce runoff and accelerate the intake of rainfall into the soil. Rainfall that does not run off evaporates into the air, is used by plants, or percolates down through the soil to the ground-water table. In some areas, water tables are falling because withdrawal rates exceed the natural recharge. Any increase in natural recharge resulting from decreased runoff automatically enhances possibilities for the sound development of water resources.

RON J. GADDIS

FARM SUPPLIES

Increasing agricultural production and mechanization have been accompanied by an increased dependence upon purchased supplies such as fertilizer, chemicals, commercial feed, petroleum, and farm equipment. The use of these farm supplies is mirrored in increases in cash farm expenses (graph 2.3). Total expenses rose nearly five-fold, from $707 million to $3.3 billion,

between 1950 and 1973. Expenditures for fertilizer increased nearly thirty-two times, feed by nearly six times, and miscellaneous supplies (including pesticides, short-term interest, utilities, and a wide range of services) by nearly eight times.

The state's agriculture accounted for approximately 5 percent of all U.S. farm production expenses during 1973. Feed and fertilizer purchases represented 4.9 and 11.1 percent, respectively, of total U.S. farm purchases.

Fertilizer

Continued agricultural growth has been accompanied by steady increases in fertilizer consumption (fig. 2.5) as more acres have been brought under fertilization and application rates on previously fertilized land have increased. The shifting of acreage from dryland to irrigated production, which took place at the rate of more than 200,000 acres per year from 1965 to 1975, required a greater use of fertilizer. Future use, however,

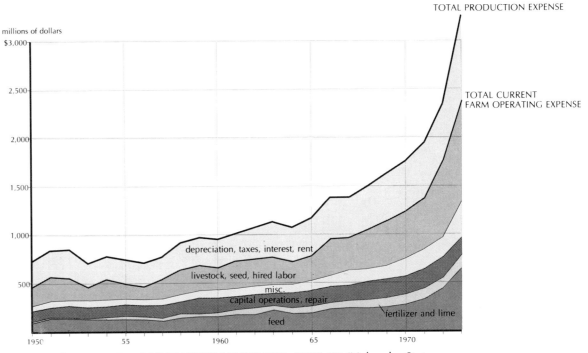

Graph 2.3. FARM PRODUCTION EXPENSES, 1950–73 (Nebraska State–Federal Division of Agricultural Statistics)

22

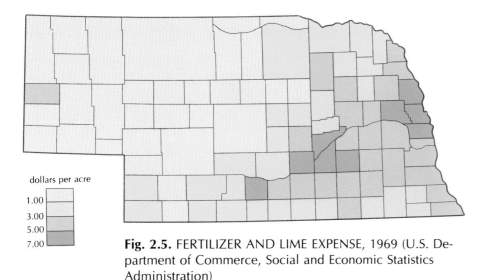

dollars per acre

1.00
3.00
5.00
7.00

Fig. 2.5. FERTILIZER AND LIME EXPENSE, 1969 (U.S. Department of Commerce, Social and Economic Statistics Administration)

may be tempered by economic considerations. Rates of application and the acreage fertilized will depend on the cost of fertilizer, feed requirements, levels of soil fertility, expected crop prices, timing of spring plantings, and field conditions for application equipment.

Fertilizer expenditures in the North Platte River area are affected by the concentration of irrigated land, rainfall patterns, and the emphasis on specialty crops grown there. Fertilizer consumption for crops grown on rolling uplands in the eastern one-third of the state is relatively stable because the region generally receives sufficient rainfall. In south-central Nebraska, fertilizer expenditures are related to the concentration of irrigated land, and irrigation development in western and Sandhills counties is increasing fertilizer expenditures in those areas. Total fertilizer expenditures for the state were an

estimated $340,000 in 1945, stood at $20 million in 1955, rose to $52 million by the end of the decade, and exceeded $200 million in 1974.

A leading source of increased crop yields, commercial fertilizer grew rapidly in importance during the decade after World War II. Nitrogen is the dominant fertilizer material and currently accounts for approximately 75 percent of the total fertilizer tonnage used in the state. Phosphorus fertilizers rank second in use. Nebraska's soils—predominantly deep, fertile, well-drained loess—require the major nutrients, nitrogen and phosphorus. Other soils that are sandy, calcareous, saline, or that are shallow because of a high water table require other nutrients as well.

Large manufacturers transport fertilizer to the state by barge, railroad, and underground pipeline systems. Most of it is

moved from terminals to retail outlets and then to farms by truck. Anhydrous ammonia production has been the only fertilizer manufacturing of significance within the state, although at several locations various other materials are processed into fertilizers for direct application on cropland.

More fertilizer is used on corn than on any other single crop because of the large acreage on which it is grown and because 93 percent of it receives commercial fertilizer. Grain sorghum is second in fertilizer use, with an estimated 80 percent of the acreage being fertilized. The full acreage of sugar beets and field beans is fertilized. Overall, approximately 40 percent of the wheat acreage is fertilized, but a much higher percentage of that in eastern Nebraska is treated than in western counties. About 25 percent of the soybean acreage receives fertilizer.

Chemicals

Nebraska farmers and ranchers spent an estimated $19.7 million on farm chemicals in 1969. Weed control in crops accounted for more than half that total, $10.4 million, and involved the largest acreage, 3.5 million acres. Insecticides used on crops (excluding hay) were the next largest chemical cost item: 2.4 million acres were treated at a cost of $6.5 million. Another $1.4 million was spent in controlling insects on livestock and poultry. The costs of chemical purchases ranged from one cent per acre of farm land in Grant and Hooker Counties to $4.49 in Holt County (fig. 2.6).

The acreage to which chemicals were

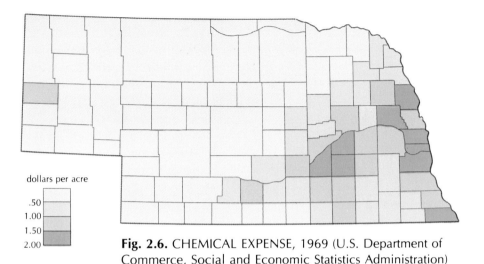

dollars per acre

.50
1.00
1.50
2.00

Fig. 2.6. CHEMICAL EXPENSE, 1969 (U.S. Department of Commerce, Social and Economic Statistics Administration)

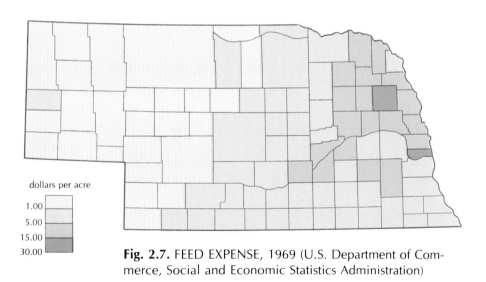

dollars per acre

1.00
5.00
15.00
30.00

Fig. 2.7. FEED EXPENSE, 1969 (U.S. Department of Commerce, Social and Economic Statistics Administration)

applied increased substantially between 1964 and 1969: for weed control in crops, from 2.0 to 3.5 million acres; for weed and brush control in pastures, from 206,000 to 387,000; and for control of insects and diseases in crops, from 1.6 to 2.5 million. It seems likely that per acre costs, the acreage treated, and dollar outlays have increased since 1969.

Commercial Feed

Livestock and poultry producers spent $640 million for feed during 1973, 50 percent more than a year earlier, six times more than in 1950. Feed costs accounted for nearly 27 percent of current farm operating expenses in 1973, almost 20 percent of total production expenses.

Feed purchases vary widely from one area of the state to another, depending primarily on the intensity of feeding operations (fig. 2.7). During 1969, livestock and poultry feed purchases in Nebraska totaled more than $306 million, of which $118.2 million went for commercially mixed formula feeds. Costs of those feeds ranged from 23 cents per acre of farm land in Arthur County to $28.31 in Sarpy County.

While much of the increase in dollar sales is accounted for by rising prices, the tonnage of commercial feeds sold at retail in Nebraska has also grown steadily. The amount sold in 1974—1.78 million tons— was 67.7 percent greater than the 1964 tonnage. Cattle feeds rank first in sales and typically have accounted for about 38 or 39 percent of the tonnage. Hog feeds are second in volume at about 29 percent, while poultry feeds have gradually declined in relative importance, from nearly 12 percent in 1964 to less than 5 percent in 1974. "Other" feeds, unidentified as to disposition, account for the remaining volume.

While the number of retail firms selling feed has decreased in recent years, the annual sales volume has expanded substantially. In 1948 there were 242 "hay, grain and feed dealers" in the state with total sales of $28 million. By 1958 the number of such firms had peaked at 418, while annual sales stood at $50 million. In 1967 there were only 328 dealers with annual sales of $115 million.

Nebraska supports an important primary feed-manufacturing industry. In 1969 there were 343 establishments (a business firm may own more than one establishment) producing 1,000 tons or more of primary feed products each, for a total output of 3.6 million tons. They employed more than 2,000 people. These establishments utilized various outlets for their products; some used several distribution channels. Of the total, 79 were wholesalers, 132 were retailers, 61 did custom feeding, 119 fed animals owned by the manufacturer, and 219 were engaged in custom grinding and mixing operations. The greatest tonnage, 28 percent, went into wholesale markets; more than 19 percent was retailed directly to users; custom grinding and mixing accounted for almost 22 percent; while custom feeding and feeding of animals owned by the manufacturer accounted for about 11 and 20 percent, respectively.

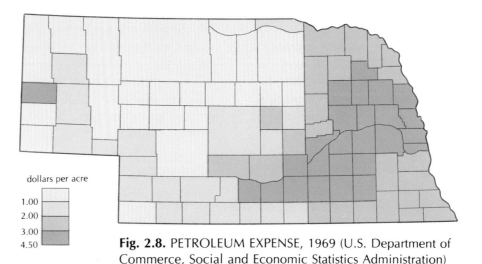

Fig. 2.8. PETROLEUM EXPENSE, 1969 (U.S. Department of Commerce, Social and Economic Statistics Administration)

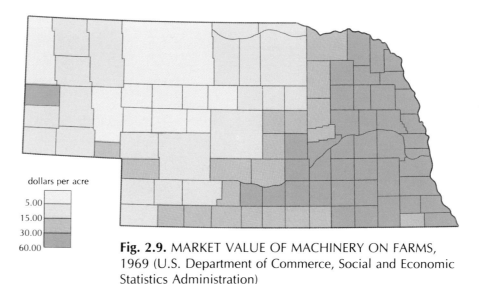

Fig. 2.9. MARKET VALUE OF MACHINERY ON FARMS, 1969 (U.S. Department of Commerce, Social and Economic Statistics Administration)

Petroleum

The state's farming and ranching industry consumed more than $77 million worth of gasoline and other petroleum products in 1969. Expenditures that year were nearly 63 percent above those for 1949, when they stood at slightly more than $47 million. Costs of petroleum purchases for agricultural production ranged from 19 cents per acre of farm land in Hitchcock County to $4.27 in York County (fig. 2.8).

The estimated 1973 fuel usage for cropping, farm-to-market transportation, and related farm activities totaled almost 90 million gallons of gasoline and nearly 58 million gallons of diesel fuel. Irrigation accounted for another 45.5 million gallons of diesel fuel, 60.7 million gallons of L.P. gas, 3,414 million cubic feet of natural gas, and 567.6 million kilowatt hours of electricity.

The estimated total 1973 energy requirements for agricultural use included 943.6 million kilowatt hours of electricity, 3,414 million cubic feet of natural gas, 185.7 million gallons of L.P. gas, 89.9 million gallons of gasoline, and 104.1 million gallons of diesel fuel.

Farm Machinery and Equipment

The value of all farm machinery and equipment on Nebraska farms and ranches at the end of 1969 was estimated at $928.7 million (fig. 2.9). The 354 farm equipment dealers in the state sold $239.9 million worth of equipment in 1972. By comparison, in 1948 there were 762 dealers with a total sales volume of $97.7 million; thus, in 1972 less than half the number of dealers had a tenfold greater total sales volume than in 1948.

The increasing average size of farms as well as of tractors and other items of farm equipment has led to a decline in the number of equipment units on Nebraska farms. For example, the state's farmers had 159,977 tractors in 1954, 180,423 in 1964, but only 147,700 in 1974. The number of combines declined from 59,572 in 1954 to 28,200 in 1974. The number of farm motor trucks, on the other hand, has increased from 72,000 in 1954 to 98,300 in 1974.

DALE G. ANDERSON
RICHARD A. WIESE

3
Nature and
Characteristics of
Farming

There is little doubt that Nebraska is an agricultural state when one looks at land use: over 93 percent of the approximately 48,949,000 acres of land in the state is in farms and ranches. Urban areas, highways, state-owned institutions, wildlife refuges, and other such uses account for less than 5 percent of the total area. Only 2 percent of the land is classified as forest.

Approximately half (23,379,000 acres) of the land in farms and ranches is classified as cropland (fig. 3.1). Nearly all the rest is in grass—the basis for Nebraska's feeder cattle production. Less than 3 percent is devoted to other uses.

Most of the grassland is in the northern and northwestern portions of the state, approximately half of the total in the Sandhills, and another 2 to 3 million acres in the extreme northwest corner of the state, where the topography and sparse rainfall limit cultivation. The rest of the grassland—some 6 million acres—is scattered throughout the state along creeks and rivers and on lands too wet or too rough to farm.

Types of Farming

Although a number of factors have influenced the types of farming that have developed within the state, soils and precipitation have undoubtedly been the most important determinants. The various types of farming regions are shown in figure 3.2.

At the extreme eastern end of the state, farming is much the same as in the corn belt; corn, soybeans, alfalfa, and some wheat and oats are the most important crops. Cattle feeding and hog production are the main livestock enterprises in the northeastern corner of the state, where a high proportion of the feed grains produced are fed. In southeastern Nebraska, livestock production is less intensive and accounts for a much smaller proportion of total crop and

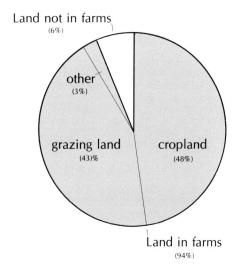

Land not in farms
(6%)

other
(3%)

grazing land
(43)%

cropland
(48%)

Land in farms
(94%)

Fig. 3.1. BASIC LAND USE IN NEBRASKA (U.S. Department of Agriculture)

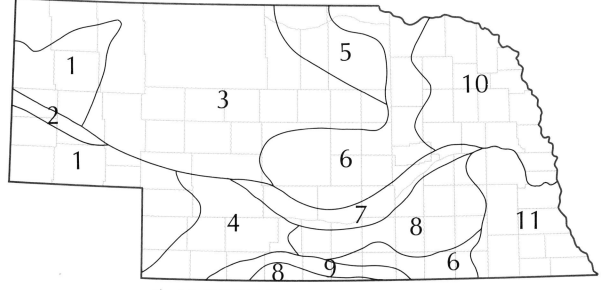

Fig. 3.2. FARMING REGIONS

1 Fallow wheat and ranching
2 Intensive irrigated crops
3 Cattle ranching
4 Livestock and fallow cropping
5 Transition from ranching to cropping (some irrigation)
6 Transition area from cornbelt-type farming to extensive cropping and ranching
7 Irrigated feed crops and cattle feeding
8 Deep-well irrigation—corn and grain sorghum
9 Irrigated feed crops and livestock production
10 Intensive livestock—cattle feeding and hog production
11 General crop and livestock farming

livestock sales.

In the east-south-central part of the state and along the Platte and Republican Rivers, irrigation is the outstanding characteristic, although nearly every farm has some land that is cropped without the benefit of irrigation. Most of the water used for irrigation is pumped from wells and is used for the production of corn. The two most important dryland crops are grain sorghum and wheat. Livestock production is comparatively unimportant in this area; only 20–30 percent of the feed grain production is fed within the county where it is produced.

North and south of the deep-well irrigation area is a transitional type of farming. Annual precipitation ranges from about 20 to 24 inches and is marginal for corn. There is comparatively little irrigation, so most of the crop production is on nonirrigated land. The two predominant crops are grain sorghum and wheat; alfalfa is the primary forage crop. A large proportion of the farms in this area have some nontillable land which is used for pasture to support small herds of beef cows. Other kinds of livestock production vary from farm to farm, but are usually on a small scale.

In the northeast corner of the Sandhills, there has been a tremendous development of center-pivot irrigation in recent years. The transition from cattle ranching to irrigated corn production has taken place in a very short period of time and the nature of agricultural production there is still changing.

In southwestern Nebraska, there is an area characterized by flat tablelands separated by deep canyons. The tablelands are used largely for cropland, with wheat and grain sorghum the principal crops. Much of this land is fallowed either every other year or every third year. The canyons are used as pasture, primarily for beef cows.

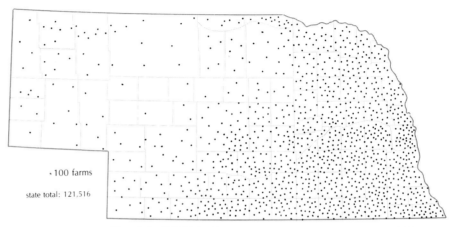

· 100 farms

state total: 121,516

Fig. 3.3. TOTAL FARMS, 1900 (U.S. Department of Commerce, Social and Economic Statistics Administration)

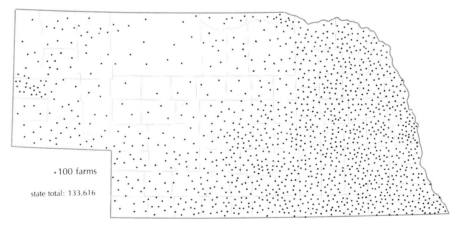

· 100 farms

state total: 133,616

Fig. 3.4. TOTAL FARMS, 1935 (U.S. Department of Commerce, Social and Economic Statistics Administration)

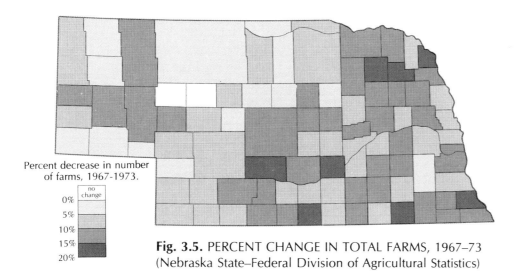

Percent decrease in number
of farms, 1967-1973.

0%
5%
10%
15%
20%

no
change

Fig. 3.5. PERCENT CHANGE IN TOTAL FARMS, 1967–73
(Nebraska State–Federal Division of Agricultural Statistics)

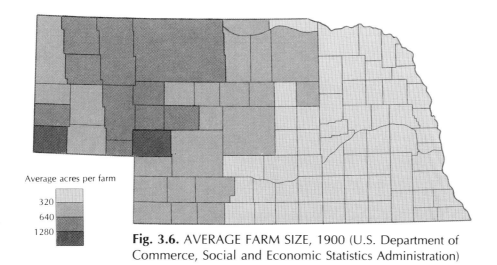

Average acres per farm

320
640
1280

Fig. 3.6. AVERAGE FARM SIZE, 1900 (U.S. Department of
Commerce, Social and Economic Statistics Administration)

The Sandhills and the rougher lands in northwestern Nebraska are devoted principally to cattle ranching. During the last few years, some center-pivot irrigation has been developed in various parts of the Sandhills, but most of the land in that area is used for grazing or for native hay production. The ranching operations vary considerably: some ranchers devote all of their resources to the production of feeder calves which are sold in October and November each year; others keep part or all of their calves, winter them over, and sell them as long yearlings in late summer or early fall. A few ranchers keep no cows but instead buy calves at weaning time, winter them, and sell them as feeders off grass in late summer or early fall approximately one year after buying them.

The most concentrated production of winter wheat is in the southern Panhandle and the counties just east of Colorado. The annual precipitation there is not adequate in most years for corn or grain sorghum. Nearly all of the wheat is produced on an every-other-year basis, with the land being fallowed in alternate years. Although some farmers produce nothing but wheat, others use nontillable land as pasture and grow some forage for the support of a beef herd.

The most intensive crop production area in the state is in Scotts Bluff and Morrill Counties in the Panhandle. Sugar beets and dry edible beans are the most important crops in that region, although some corn and alfalfa is also produced. Small cattle-feeding enterprises can be found on many of the farms, and some lambs are also fed in this area.

Number of Farms

The first farms were established in Nebraska shortly before the Civil War. The census of 1860 recorded 3,000 farms, and the number increased rapidly during the next thirty years. By 1900 there were 122,000 farms (fig. 3.3) and the 1910 census listed 130,000. From 1910 to 1920, there was a slight decrease, and it was not until 1935 that the number reached the all-time high of 134,000 (fig. 3.4). The number has declined steadily since then (fig. 3.5). Although the census shows an increasing total acreage in farms and ranches until 1945, for all practical purposes it has been fairly stable since 1935.

Size of Farming Operations·

The average size of farms and ranches has increased steadily since 1880. During those very early years most farms were 160 acres, largely because that was the acreage available under the terms of the Homestead Act. By 1900, however, the average size had increased to 246 acres (fig. 3.6). In 1935, when farm numbers were at or near their peak, the average size had reached 349 acres (fig. 3.7). By 1969, the average size of farms and ranches was 634 acres—almost twice that in 1935 (fig. 3.8). The size of farms and ranches has increased since 1969 and undoubtedly will continue to do so for some years to come.

Farm size is affected by rainfall and soil and water resources, and is smaller in eastern Nebraska, where the annual precipita-

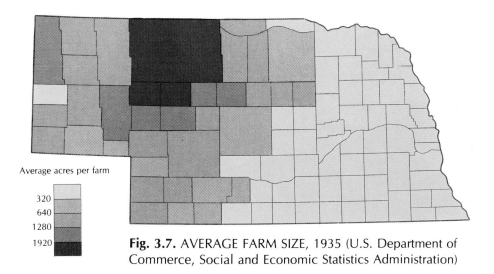

Average acres per farm

320
640
1280
1920

Fig. 3.7. AVERAGE FARM SIZE, 1935 (U.S. Department of Commerce, Social and Economic Statistics Administration)

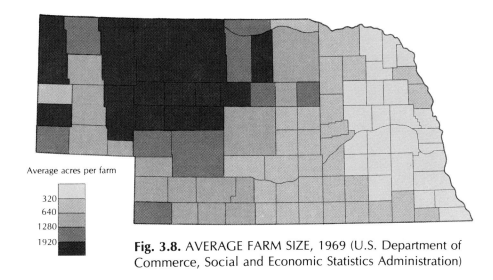

Average acres per farm

320
640
1280
1920

Fig. 3.8. AVERAGE FARM SIZE, 1969 (U.S. Department of Commerce, Social and Economic Statistics Administration)

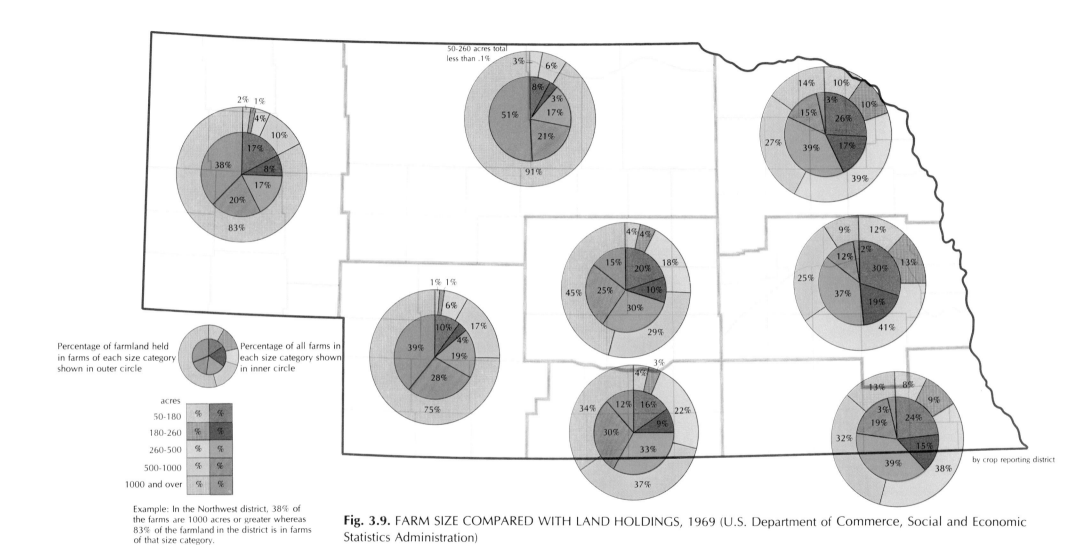

50-260 acres total
less than .1%

Percentage of farmland held
in farms of each size category
shown in outer circle

Percentage of all farms in
each size category shown
in inner circle

acres
50-180
180-260
260-500
500-1000
1000 and over

Example: In the Northwest district, 38% of
the farms are 1000 acres or greater whereas
83% of the farmland in the district is in farms
of that size category.

by crop reporting district

Fig. 3.9. FARM SIZE COMPARED WITH LAND HOLDINGS, 1969 (U.S. Department of Commerce, Social and Economic
Statistics Administration)

tion is 24 inches or more and the soils and topography are suitable for cultivation. More intensive kinds of farming have developed in that area.

In south-central Nebraska, where soils and topography are particularly favorable for widespread irrigation, the trend toward farm enlargement has slowed.

When the state's farms are classified by size, a large proportion are in the three largest categories (fig. 3.9). More than half of the total number of farms in every crop-reporting district are 260 acres or larger. In eastern Nebraska 50–60 percent are in the three largest categories, compared to 75–95 percent in western Nebraska.

Approximately 25 percent of the farms in the three eastern crop-reporting districts are in the smallest size group—50–180 acres. Many of these are 160-acre units. In general, farms of this size do not generate enough income to provide a family with a very high level of living unless a rather intensive livestock program is involved.

The proportion of land operated by farmers and ranchers in the three largest size groups ranges from about 75 percent in eastern Nebraska to 95 percent or more in the western end of the state (fig. 3.9). A similar high proportion of total crop and livestock production comes from farms and ranches in those three largest size categories.

Wherever ranching is predominant, the ranches tend to be in the largest size group. Ranchers generally consider 200–300 cows the minimum needed to provide an acceptable level of living for a family. Because at

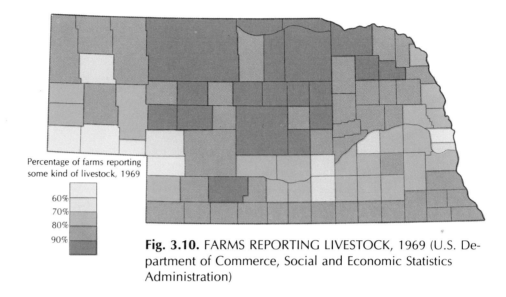

Percentage of farms reporting some kind of livestock, 1969

60%
70%
80%
90%

Fig. 3.10. FARMS REPORTING LIVESTOCK, 1969 (U.S. Department of Commerce, Social and Economic Statistics Administration)

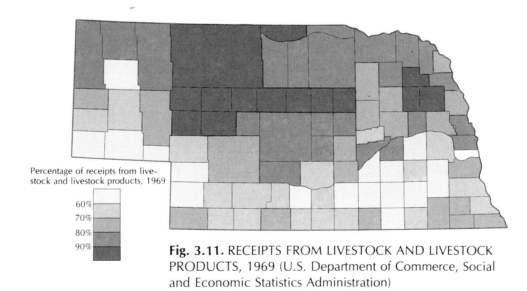

Percentage of receipts from live-stock and livestock products, 1969

60%
70%
80%
90%

Fig. 3.11. RECEIPTS FROM LIVESTOCK AND LIVESTOCK PRODUCTS, 1969 (U.S. Department of Commerce, Social and Economic Statistics Administration)

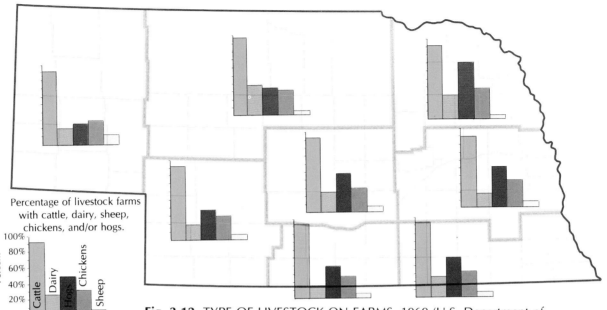

Percentage of livestock farms with cattle, dairy, sheep, chickens, and/or hogs.

Fig. 3.12. TYPE OF LIVESTOCK ON FARMS, 1969 (U.S. Department of Commerce, Social and Economic Statistics Administration)

least 10–15 acres are required to support each cow, even the smallest ranches are usually 2,000 acres or more in size; very few are smaller than that.

Where the farming depends mostly on cultivated crops, the introduction of tractors and related equipment and the development of larger machinery has encouraged farm enlargement. Price-cost relationships have also had an important effect on size, particularly during the period 1951–71, when the prices received by farmers declined in relation to the prices paid for production items. At the same time, the cost of living was steadily increasing, so it was necessary for farmers to increase their total production to

maintain the same level of buying power.

Livestock

Cash receipts from the sale of livestock make up 65–75 percent of total receipts from farm marketings on Nebraska farms and ranches. In northeastern and north-central Nebraska, the extreme southeastern corner of the state, the southern tier of counties, and several counties in the northwest, eight out of ten farms raised livestock in 1969 (fig. 3.10). In much of the south-central portion of the state, however, only 60–80 percent of the farmers reported livestock; and in the most intensive wheat-pro-

ducing counties, less than 60 percent of the farmers reported livestock.

Receipts from livestock in 1969 made up 90 percent or more of total farm marketings on ranches and 80–90 percent in the northeast, but accounted for no more than 50–70 percent in the southern part of the state and averaged less than 60 percent in the intensive wheat-producing counties (fig. 3.11).

Of the farmers who reported livestock in 1969, 90 percent in every crop-reporting district in the state reported some cattle (fig. 3.12). Hogs were next most commonly reported: 50 percent or more of the farms in eastern Nebraska and more than 70 percent in the northeastern part of the state reported

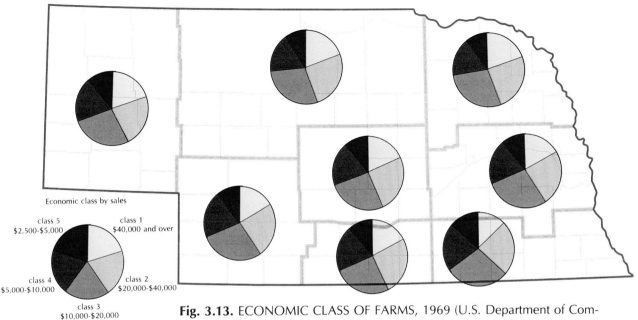

Economic class by sales

class 5
$2,500-$5,000

class 1
$40,000 and over

class 4
$5,000-$10,000

class 2
$20,000-$40,000

class 3
$10,000-$20,000

proportion of total

Fig. 3.13. ECONOMIC CLASS OF FARMS, 1969 (U.S. Department of Commerce, Social and Economic Statistics Administration)

some on hand. In central and southern Nebraska, hogs were reported on 40–50 percent of the farms, while about 35 percent of farmers in the north-central and southwestern areas reported them. Less than 30 percent of the farmers in the Panhandle had hogs.

Chickens were reported on 25–35 percent of the farms in every reporting district, and of those reporting them, over 90 percent had laying flocks of 400 birds or less. Dairy cattle were found on 20–40 percent of the farms with livestock. In all crop-reporting districts except the Panhandle, less than 10 percent of the farms reporting livestock had

sheep; in the Panhandle, about 15 percent reported some.

Volume of Sales

The distribution of farms by economic classes is remarkably similar from one crop-reporting district to another, regardless of differences in types of farming or farm size (fig. 3.13). Of the farmers receiving $2,500 or more from the sale of crops and livestock, one-sixth had sales of $40,000 or more in 1969, 25 percent had sales of $20,000–$39,999, and more than a fourth had sales of $10,000–$19,999. About 30

percent had sales amounting to less than $10,000.

Tenure Patterns

Tenure patterns are similar from one crop-reporting district to another (fig. 3.14). In the state as a whole, 39 percent of the farms were operated by those who owned the land—commonly referred to as full owners. About a fourth (24.6 percent) of the farms were operated by people who rented all of the land they operated. The rest, 36 percent, were operated by part-owners who farmed some rented land in addition to that which

35

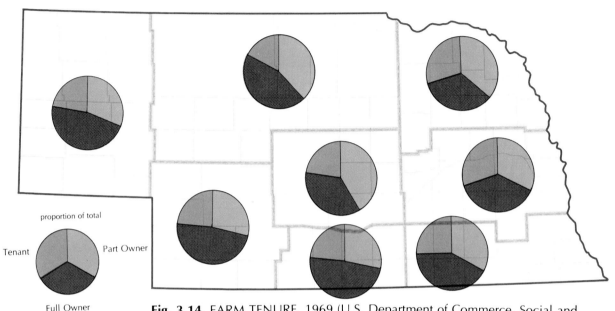

proportion of total

Tenant   Part Owner

Full Owner

Fig. 3.14. FARM TENURE, 1969 (U.S. Department of Commerce, Social and Economic Statistics Administration)

they owned. The proportion of farms operated strictly on a tenant basis was smallest in the ranching area of north-central Nebraska. Part-owner operations accounted for nearly half of the farms in the Panhandle, north-central, southwestern, and south-central areas of the state. Full ownership was most prevalent in north-central and central Nebraska.

Age of Farm Operators

The average age of farm operators in 1969 was 49. About one farm in eight was being operated by a man past 65; one-fourth of the operators were between 55 and 64; while 26 percent were from 45 to 54 years of age, and 21 percent were in the 35–44 age bracket. Less than one farm in six was operated by someone under 35. There was very little difference from one part of the state to another in the proportion of farms operated by each age group.

PHILIP A. HENDERSON

36

4
Crop Production

Nebraska is a leading state in crop production, in 1973 ranking seventh in acreage of principal crops, third in production of both corn and soghum for grain, and fourth in winter wheat and hay production. Crop production is the foundation of the state's agricultural industry. The abundant supply of feed grains and forages forms the basis for the more than $2.4 billion livestock industry, and crops, together with livestock, provide both raw materials for the state's food- and feed-processing industries and products for export.

The leading field crops by value in 1973 were corn, wheat, sorghum, hay, and soybeans, in that order (fig. 4.1). Sugar beets, dry beans, the lesser small grains (oats, rye, barley, and millets), and potatoes also contributed significantly to agricultural sales, while miscellaneous crops were important in local areas.

Receipts from crop marketing increased twenty-five-fold from 1932, when they hit bottom, to 1971; then they more than doubled in two years (graph 4.1). Cash receipts from crops ranged from 28 to 42 percent of the total farm marketings between 1943 and 1973 and in 1973 accounted for 40 percent of the total agricultural income. However, the value of crops, including those feed grains harvested and fed on the farms where produced, was $2.4 billion, or 58 percent of the total income. In addition, the value of corn and sorghum for silage and forage was estimated at more than $100 million, crop residues at $56 million, and feed from pasture and range at another $381 million.

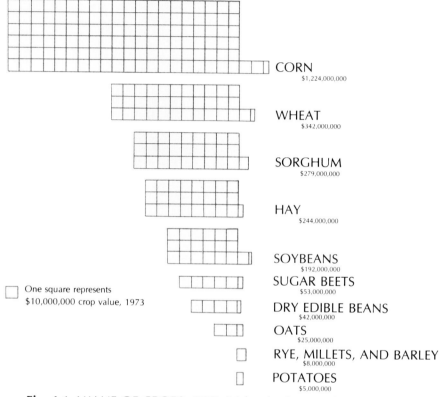

Fig. 4.1. VALUE OF CROPS, 1973 (Nebraska State–Federal Division of Agricultural Statistics)

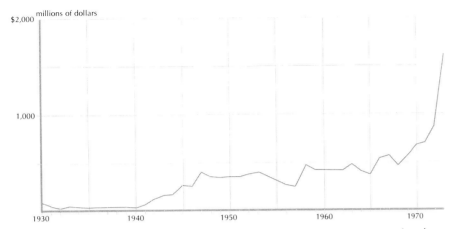

millions of dollars

$2,000

1,000

1930   1940   1950   1960   1970

Graph 4.1. RECEIPTS FROM CROP MARKETING, 1930–73 (Nebraska State–Federal Division of Agricultural Statistics)

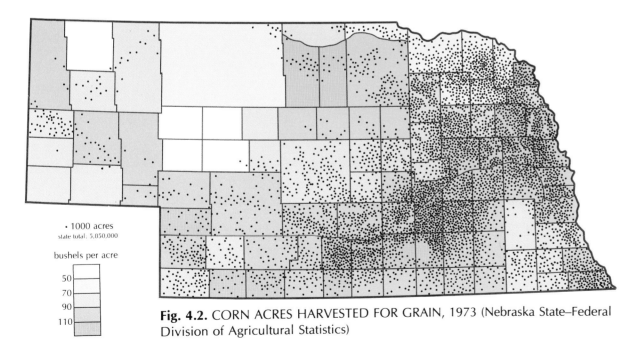

• 1000 acres
state total: 5,850,000

bushels per acre

50
70
90
110

Fig. 4.2. CORN ACRES HARVESTED FOR GRAIN, 1973 (Nebraska State–Federal Division of Agricultural Statistics)

CORN

Corn is the most important crop grown in Nebraska. It is harvested on twice as many acres and contributes to the economy nearly four times as much as any other crop. The value of corn for grain, $1.2 billion, was 51 percent of the total for all crops in 1973. Corn accounts for 80 percent of all feed grains, the basis of the livestock industry. About a third of the corn grown for grain, plus corn silage from some one-half million acres, is fed to livestock on the farms where it is produced.

Corn is grown in almost every county, but the largest acreage and the highest production are in the northeast, east, and south-central areas and along the river valleys (fig. 4.2). Corn is primarily a nonirrigated crop in the eastern third of the state, while as much as 90 percent is irrigated in south-central, southwestern, northern, and Panhandle counties (fig. 4.3). The expansion of corn acreage into the southwestern and Sandhills areas has resulted largely from the development in the late 1960s and early 1970s of center-pivot irrigation systems, which permit the irrigation of rolling land and sandy soil.

The predominant irrigated crop, corn was harvested on 62 percent of all irrigated cropland in 1973. Nearly one-half of the corn acreage is irrigated, and that acreage accounted for 57 percent of the production in 1973 and 82 percent in 1974, a drought year. The amount of corn produced under irrigation increased threefold from 1964 to

39

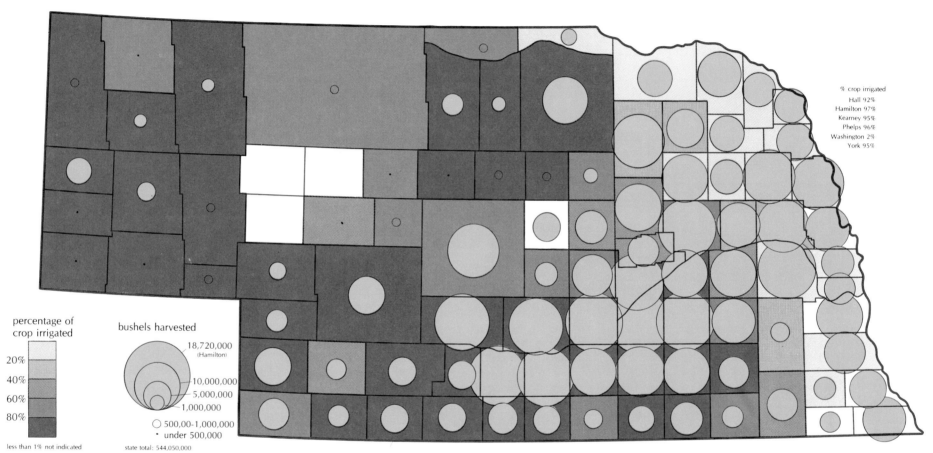

percentage of
crop irrigated

bushels harvested

20%

40%

60%

80%

18,720,000
(Hamilton)

10,000,000
5,000,000
1,000,000

○ 500,00-1,000,000
· under 500,000

less than 1% not indicated

state total: 544,050,000

Fig. 4.3. CORN FOR GRAIN PRODUCTION, 1973 (Nebraska State–Federal Division of Agricultural Statistics)

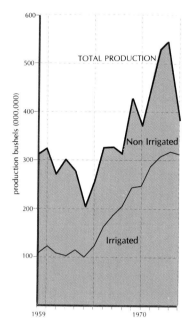

Graph 4.2. CORN PRODUCTION, 1959–74 (Nebraska State–Federal Division of Agricultural Statistics)

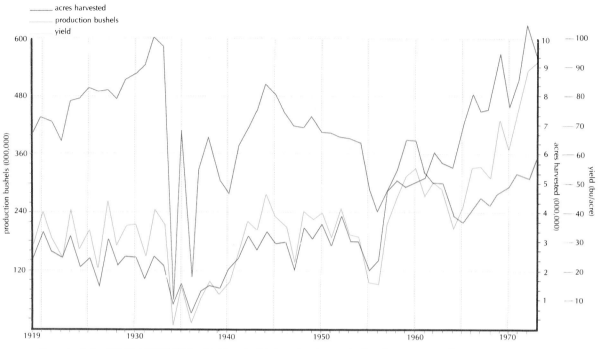

Graph 4.3. CORN TRENDS, 1919–73 (Nebraska State–Federal Division of Agricultural Statistics)

1973 as the number of irrigated acres planted to corn increased from 1.34 million to 2.99 million (graph 4.2). Irrigation has contributed to higher yields per acre—113 bushels, compared to 75.4 bushels for non-irrigated corn in 1973 and 93 bushels, compared to 26 bushels in 1974—and has resulted in more stable production with less annual fluctuation in yields.

Corn was the most important crop to the homesteaders who settled in eastern Nebraska, and by 1890 the state contributed 10 percent of the nation's production. Corn

acreage stood at 6.7 million acres by 1919 and continued to increase until 1932, when more than 10 million acres were harvested (graph 4.3). Less than 1 million acres were harvested in the severe drought year of 1934. The general decline in corn acreage during the 1940s and 1950s coincided with an increase in sorghum acreage. Corn acreage increases since 1964 have been on land under irrigation; the nonirrigated corn acreage continued to decline through 1974. Consequently, a major shift in the location of crop acreage has occurred, especially in

the lower rainfall areas south of the Platte River, where corn is predominant on irrigated land and sorghum on nonirrigated land.

Increased corn yields have been phenomenal and clearly demonstrate the advances in agricultural technology that have occurred in Nebraska. Prior to the mid-1950s, the average yield of corn for grain ranged from 38 bushels per acre in 1952 to 5.5 bushels in 1934 (graph 4.3). Since 1955 yields have steadily increased, reaching a record high of 104 bushels per acre in

41

1972. Several factors have contributed to this impressive record. The steady addition of land under irrigation, with a major share being planted to corn, and the shift of non-irrigated corn acreage to sorghum and soybeans greatly increased the average corn yield. The use of nitrogen fertilizer increased sevenfold between 1955 and 1974, with most of it being used on corn, and the application of chemical pesticides to control weeds and insects expanded greatly. By 1950 nearly all of the Nebraska acreage was planted to hybrid corn, and the substantial yield increases since the early 1960s are associated with single-cross and modified single-cross hybrids that respond to increased soil fertility, adequate soil moisture, and good management. Improved machinery for more accurate placement of seed and for more efficient harvesting gradually became available (nearly 75 percent of the crop is harvested as shelled corn). With few exceptions (1964, 1970, and 1974) favorable weather conditions have prevailed, making possible high yields on nonirrigated land receiving good soil and crop management.

Special Types of Corn

Nearly all of the corn grown in Nebraska as a feed grain is dent corn, so called because the soft starch in the center of the kernel dries at a differential rate, causing the characteristic dent. Other types are produced on a limited basis.

Nebraska ranked third in the nation in popcorn production in 1973 with 83 million pounds. Popcorn production has fluctuated from year to year but gained more prominence from 1964 to 1974. The highest production and acreage were in 1974, when 119 million pounds were produced from 34,000 acres. The crop is usually produced under contract. Popcorn is grown mainly in several eastern counties, although some is raised in the Sandhills area under center-pivot irrigation.

High-lysine and waxy corn are dent types of special nutritional value in feeding livestock. They are generally produced and fed on livestock farms in the eastern and south-central areas of the state. White corn production was limited to 17,000 acres in 1973 but some is marketed each year, primarily for human consumption. Sweet corn is often produced near urban centers for local markets and is widely grown in gardens for home use.

J. H. WILLIAMS

Nearly 50 percent of Nebraska's corn is produced under irrigation.

GRAIN SORGHUM

Grain sorghum is a cereal closely related to forage sorghum, sudangrass, broomcorn, and the weed johnsongrass. Its popular name, milo, stems from an earlier period when the true milos, a specific type of sorghum, were grown. Grain sorghum varieties were formerly pure lines like wheat or soybeans but now are hybrids like corn.

The grain of sorghum resembles corn chemically and nutritionally. Nearly all of it is fed to livestock or poultry, although it can be milled for starch, used as a brewer's grain, or distilled for alcohol. There is current interest in sorghum grain as a source for "gasahol," a gasoline-alcohol blend.

Grain sorghum is a relative newcomer to Nebraska. Not until 1932 was as much as 5,000 acres harvested (graph 4.4). Varieties then were late and tall, and heads were topped by hand. The subsequent development of earlier-maturing, combine varieties helped promote the crop, which became established in Nebraska by 1940. Production in 1930 was 64,000 bushels compared to 462,000 in 1935 and 5,104,000 in 1940. Production declined during and after World War II but surged again during the drought of the 1950s and began to increase dramatically in 1957, the first year hybrids were widely grown.

Since 1957, more than 75 million bushels per year have been produced, except in 1959, 1961, and 1974. The highest production—nearly 140 million bushels—was in

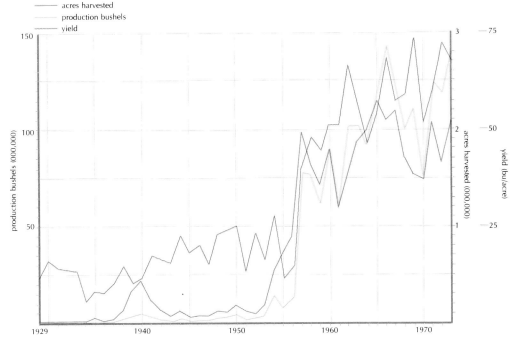

acres harvested
production bushels
yield

Graph 4.4. SORGHUM TRENDS, 1929–73 (Nebraska State–Federal Division of Agricultural Statistics)

1966; 1974 production was down to 64 million. The highest yields were obtained in 1969 (73.0 bushels per acre) and in 1972 (72.0). Yields in 1974 averaged only 33.0 bushels per acre, but that was considerably above the yields of 5.7–14.0 bushels per acre obtained during the drought years of the 1930s and 1955 and 1956.

Since 1954 Nebraska has consistently ranked third in the nation as a grain sorghum–producing state. The number of harvested acres in recent years has generally

ranged from 1.5 to 2.0 million. The crop is produced primarily in southeast and south-central Nebraska south of the Platte River (fig. 4.4 and 4.5). Production is limited elsewhere but extends northeast to South Dakota and southwest to Colorado.

Most of the Nebraska crop is planted from mid May to early June. Earlier plantings cannot tolerate cool weather, while later plantings have difficulty maturing before frost. Seedbed preparation and planting are similar to that for corn and soybeans. Much

grain sorghum is planted in thirty-inch rows like corn but not as deep. Plant populations of 50,000 or more per acre are used in the east but in the west they are sparser except under irrigation, where they usually number about 100,000. Planting rates are not nearly so critical as with some crops, for sorghum tillers under favorable conditions and compensates when stands are suboptimum.

Sorghum responds to rainfall and water, but only 10–15 percent of the crop is irrigated. The plant is naturally more heat and drought tolerant than corn and is confined largely to dryland culture. It tends to go dormant under unfavorable conditions and revives when they again become favorable. Interestingly, sorghum withstands flooding better than corn.

Fertilizers are commonly used on sorghum, particularly nitrogen as a preplanting application, as a side dressing during early growth, or both. Phosphates and minor elements are used where needed. Barnyard and feedlot manure are becoming more important as fertilizer.

Herbicides are widely used for weed control, often in conjunction with cultivation. Chemical weed control, fertilizers, better tillage and planting methods, and the introduction of hybrids all have contributed to increased production.

Aside from weeds and weather, production hazards include diseases and insects, although they are less serious than in states south of Nebraska. In the late 1960s the sorghum greenbug, an aphid, became endemic, but it has been brought under control by chemicals and the development of resistant

43

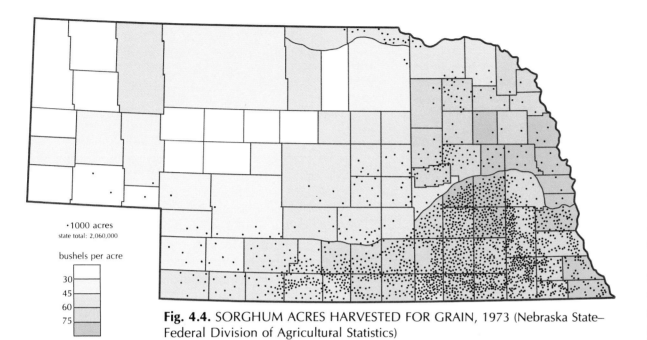

·1000 acres
state total: 2,060,000

bushels per acre

30	
45	
60	
75	

Fig. 4.4. SORGHUM ACRES HARVESTED FOR GRAIN, 1973 (Nebraska State–Federal Division of Agricultural Statistics)

hybrids. Birds also like to eat grain sorghum in the fields and can be a local problem.

The grain crop is generally combine harvested after a killing frost, which helps dry the plants. Muddy fields, lodged stalks, and high-moisture grain can be problems at this time. The remaining stubble is grazed by cattle if weather permits, or it may be collected and stacked for winter roughage. Much of the grain has been artificially dried in the past, but the high cost and decreased availability of fuel are promoting greater interest in the storage of high-moisture grain and in making silage of the entire grain sorghum plant.

Harvested grain is either stored on the farm or trucked directly to commercial feedyards or elevators. Some is shipped to other states, and some goes for export. Unlike other cereals, grain sorghum is sold by the hundredweight rather than the bushel. The prices received by farmers for the 1974 crop varied around $5.00 per hundredweight, which was considerably higher than in previous years.

W. M. Ross

Harvesting grain sorghum. A combine harvests the grain, leaving leaves and stalks for cattle feed.

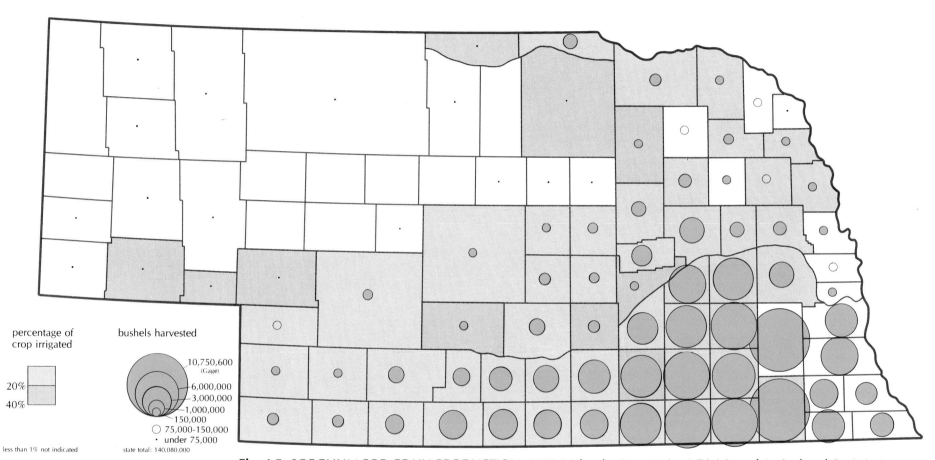

bushels harvested

10,750,600
(Gage)
6,000,000
3,000,000
1,000,000
150,000
75,000-150,000
under 75,000
state total: 140,080,000

Fig. 4.5. SORGHUM FOR GRAIN PRODUCTION, 1973 (Nebraska State–Federal Division of Agricultural Statistics)

SOYBEANS

Soybeans gained a prominent position in the state's agriculture during the 1960s as production more than doubled. In 1973 and 1974 more than 1.1 million acres were harvested (fig. 4.6). The record production of 36.3 million bushels in 1973 (fig. 4.7) ranked soybeans fifth in crop value in Nebraska and moved Nebraska into eleventh place among the states.

The history of soybean production in the state has been one of constantly increasing acreage and total production (graph 4.5). Soybeans were first grown for hay during the 1920s. From 1929 to 1946 the acreage grown for hay ranged from 1,000 acres to a high of 13,000 in 1940. Soybeans are seldom harvested for hay now except to salvage a hailed or damaged crop.

Soybean acreage increased gradually from 1938, when 1,000 acres were harvested for beans, until 1960, when 164,000 acres produced over 4.5 million bushels. By 1969, it stood at 777,000 acres and in 1974 rose to 1.2 million. The rapid increase in production after 1960 was due to an expanded domestic and foreign market demand for soybean oil and meal, which gave rise to more favorable prices. The increase in soybean acreage was accompanied by a sharp decline in oat acreage.

Average yields per acre have varied from year to year, primarily as a result of fluctuations in the amount and distribution of

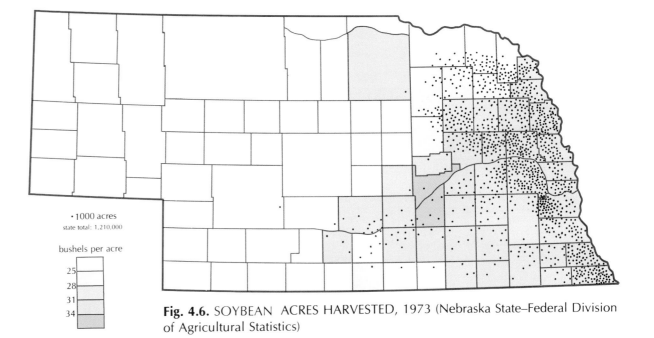

• 1000 acres
state total: 1,210,000

bushels per acre

25
28
31
34

Fig. 4.6. SOYBEAN ACRES HARVESTED, 1973 (Nebraska State–Federal Division of Agricultural Statistics)

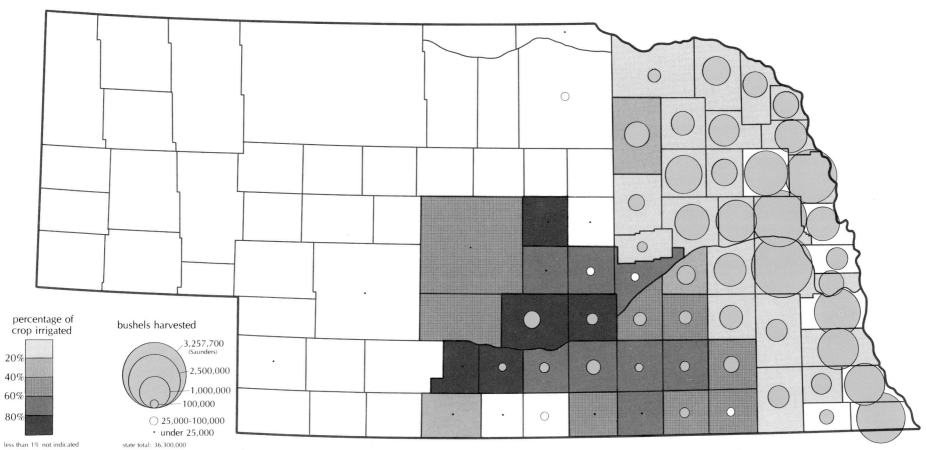

percentage of crop irrigated

20%
40%
60%
80%

less than 1% not indicated

bushels harvested

3,257,700 (Saunders)
2,500,000
1,000,000
100,000
25,000-100,000
under 25,000

state total: 36,300,000

Fig. 4.7. SOYBEAN PRODUCTION, 1973 (Nebraska State–Federal Division of Agricultural Statistics)

rainfall during the growing season. However the trend in yields has been upward (graph 4.5). The record high state average yield was 32.5 bushels per acre in 1969 and 1972. The record lows—10 bushels per acre in 1939 and 10.5 in 1955—were recorded in drought years. The highest average yields per acre for irrigated and nonirrigated soybeans, respectively, were 39.1 bushels in 1969 and 32.2 bushels in 1972. Improved cultivation practices, the introduction of higher-yielding varieties responsive to better management, and improved weed-control methods, including the use of chemical herbicides, have contributed to both higher average yields and the increase in acreage.

Soybean production is concentrated in the eastern third of the state; here in the higher rainfall area, from 95 to 97 percent are produced. Soybeans grown farther west are generally irrigated (fig. 4.7).

Soybeans are adapted to a wide range of soils but generally produce more on well-drained fine-textured soils. Coarse, sandy soils are too droughty for good production unless irrigated. On high-pH (saline or alkaline) soils like those along the river valleys, soybeans are not always highly productive, and in some fields they have produced so poorly that they are no longer grown. On more acid soils in some southeastern areas, liming is beneficial. Soybeans are legumes and, when inoculated with nitrogen-fixing bacteria, can supply a large portion of their nitrogen requirement. They usually do not give economic yield responses to high rates of nitrogen fertilizer as corn does, although exceptions have been noted on some

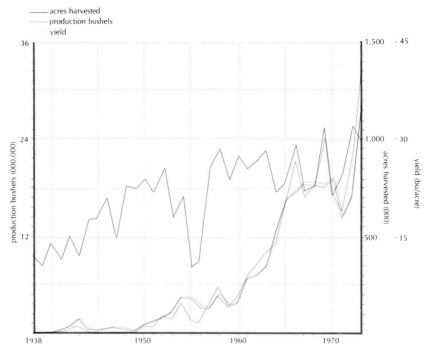

Graph 4.5. SOYBEAN TRENDS, 1938–73 (Nebraska State–Federal Division of Agricultural Statistics)

eroded soils in southeastern Nebraska. Responses to fertilizer can usually be predicted by reliable soil test analyses.

The acreage grown under irrigation since 1956 has ranged from a low of 7,000 acres in 1960, representing 4.2 percent of the total acreage, to a high of 103,000 acres, or 9.4 percent of the total, in 1974. Irrigated soybeans have accounted for 5.4–12.8 percent of the total production except in 1956, when they represented 39 percent. In that dry year the average yield of nonirrigated soybeans was only 8.2 bushels per acre,

compared to 29.9 bushels for irrigated soybeans. Soybeans generally do not respond to irrigation as corn does, with greatly increased yields. Consequently, in years of adequate amounts and favorable distribution of rainfall, the difference between average yields of irrigated and nonirrigated soybeans is small: during the ten-year period 1964–73, it averaged only 8.1 bushels per acre.

Planting of soybeans begins in early May, peaks about the first of June, and continues until mid-June. More dependable herbicides have made earlier planting possible and have resulted in increased interest in planting soybeans in narrower rows.

Flowering and podding occurs in early July through mid-August, depending upon the variety and planting time. The long flowering period enables soybeans to escape some of the adverse effects of drought or hot winds of short duration. Rainfall during late July and August when pods are filling is generally conducive to higher yields. A few fields of early-maturing varieties are ready for harvest in mid-September; the peak harvest comes in early October.

Soybeans are grown primarily for the seed, which contains 40 percent protein and 20 percent oil. The oil is used domestically for margarine, cooking oils, and other edible products as well as for industrial purposes. The meal is used primarily for livestock feed and by the broiler industry, although there is increased interest in the use of the protein for food.

J. H. WILLIAMS

Soybean harvest. The seed is threshed, loaded into trucks, and transported to elevators.

SMALL GRAINS

The small grains—wheat, oats, barley, rye, and millet—represent about 15 percent of the total crop production in Nebraska, and wheat production is a major contributor of farm cash income. The production of small grains is not confined to any one area, but is of greatest importance in the western part of the state. Weather, the extensive introduction of irrigation, farm programs, and the development of alternate crops have been significant factors in determining the total production of small grains and the year-to-year variations in production.

When Nebraska achieved statehood in 1867, only about 100,000 acres of small grains were harvested. The harvested acreage increased steadily to nearly 5 million by 1900 and slightly more than 7 million by 1918. From then until 1952 the annual acreage ranged generally from 6 to 7 million, dropping to a low in 1934, but hitting the all-time high of 7.7 million in 1938 as small grains replaced corn on many acres during the drought years.

Beginning in 1953, there was a steady decline to the current 3.5-million-acre level, largely because of the acreage restrictions of the national farm program, the introduction of hybrid sorghum, the decline in crop rotation in eastern Nebraska in favor of continuous corn production, highly favorable prices for soybeans, and the displacement of dryland small-grain production in certain areas by the extensive introduction of irrigation for corn production.

The total production of small grains in tonnage has not declined, however, but has increased despite the reduction in acreage. The 1974 crop of 3.5 million tons was produced on only 3.5 million acres, compared to the 3.1 million tons produced on 7.7 million acres in 1938. Winter wheat is currently the predominant small-grain crop, with 82 percent of the total small-grain production in 1974, compared to 61 percent in 1938.

Wheat

Wheat production in Nebraska is currently confined almost entirely to winter wheat. That was not the case before 1900; in the period 1896–1900, 87 percent of the wheat acreage was in spring wheat. From 1901 to 1905 winter wheat took over 70 percent of the acreage, and spring wheat acreage has continued to decline. The shift to winter wheat was due primarily to the superior performance of Turkey hard red winter wheat, introduced into Kansas and Nebraska

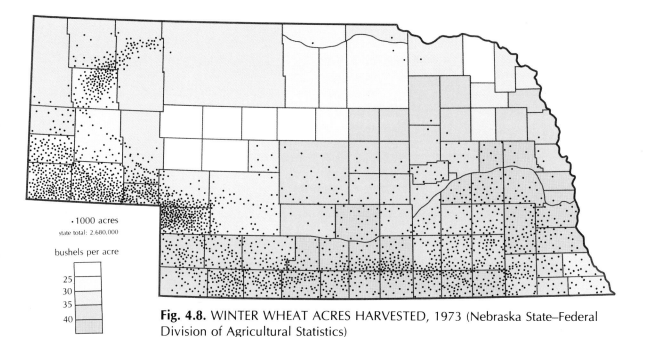

Fig. 4.8. WINTER WHEAT ACRES HARVESTED, 1973 (Nebraska State–Federal Division of Agricultural Statistics)

bushels harvested

6,216,660
(Cheyenne)

3,000,000
1,000,000
150,000
75,000-150,000
· under 75,000

state total: 93,800,000

Fig. 4.9. WINTER WHEAT PRODUCTION, 1973 (Nebraska State–Federal Division of Agricultural Statistics)

51

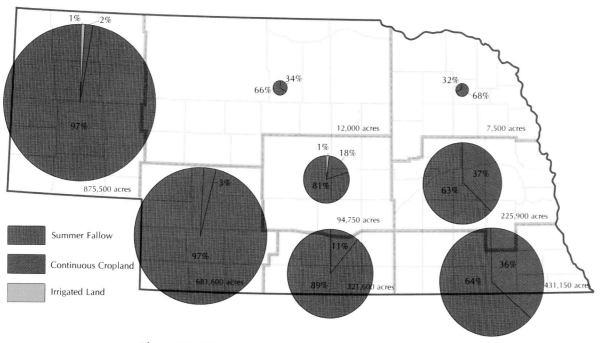

1%
2%
97%
875,500 acres

34%
66%

32%
68%

12,000 acres

7,500 acres

1%
18%
81%
94,750 acres

37%
63%
225,900 acres

3%
97%
681,600 acres

11%
89%
321,600 acres

36%
64%
431,150 acres

Summer Fallow

Continuous Cropland

Irrigated Land

Fig. 4.10. WHEAT ACRES HARVESTED BY CROPPING PRACTICE, 1973
(Nebraska State–Federal Division of Agricultural Statistics)

in 1874. Turkey wheat germ plasm is present in all of the winter wheat now grown in Nebraska. The Centurk variety released in 1971 commemorates its introduction.

The hard red winter wheat produced in Nebraska is used almost entirely for bread. It is grown in the southern half of the state and in northwestern Nebraska, with the highest production in the southwestern area and the Panhandle (figs. 4.8 and 4.9). It is seeded in September and harvested in late June and July. Summer fallowing for moisture and nitrate accumulation is standard in western Nebraska and predominates even in the eastern part of the state (fig. 4.10). Production is almost entirely on dryland. Strip cropping is used on some of the coarse-textured soils in western Nebraska.

For the ten-year period 1965–74, the harvested wheat acreage averaged 2.75 million acres, with an average production of 90.2 million bushels for a yield of 33.1 bushels per acre. The annual variation in harvested acreage and total production has been considerable (graph 4.6). The lowest years were 1917, when the production practices could not cope with a dry fall and cold, open winter, and in the 1930s during the drought. Yields have increased steadily since the 1950s except for the early 1960s, when stem rust was severe. The abandonment rate is now low because implements and cultivation practices have been improved and wheat has been eliminated from marginal land. Current popular varieties are Centurk, Scout 66, and Lancer—varieties responsive to improved crop management and resistant to stem rust disease.

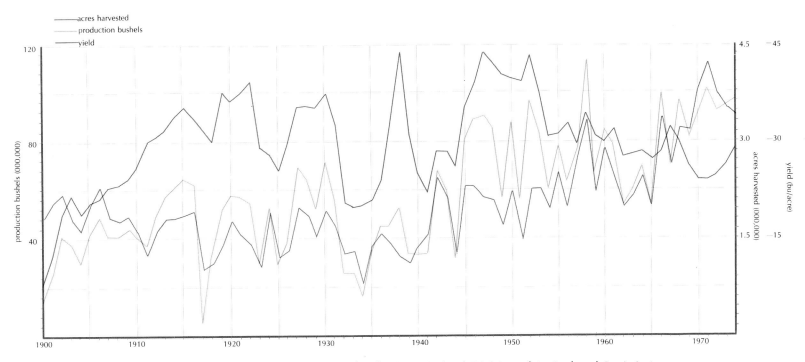

Graph 4.6. WINTER WHEAT TRENDS, 1900–1974 (Nebraska State–Federal Division of Agricultural Statistics)

Wheat is almost entirely a cash grain crop. It often is used as a feed grain when the market price approaches that of other feed grains. Some is used for fall and spring pasture, but the uncertain winter weather conditions with snow possible from November through March discourage this practice.

Oats

Spring oats are grown statewide, but production is highest in northeastern and northwestern Nebraska (figs. 4.11 and 4.12). In the western area some oats are irrigated but generally the crop is produced on dryland and often in crop rotations. Oats may be planted as a companion crop with spring-seeded legumes. They are usually used as a feed grain on the farm where grown but

may be marketed as a feed grain or as a food grain if of high quality. A considerable amount of oat straw is retained after harvest and used for animal bedding or as a roughage feed. Baled oat straw has added greatly to the value of oat production.

The continuous cropping of corn, increased planting of sorghum and soybeans, and decreased demand for oats all have combined to reduce oat acreage from the

53

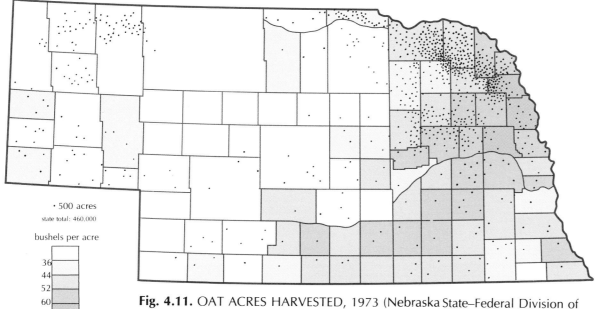

· 500 acres

state total: 460,000

bushels per acre

36
44
52
60

Fig. 4.11. OAT ACRES HARVESTED, 1973 (Nebraska State–Federal Division of Agricultural Statistics)

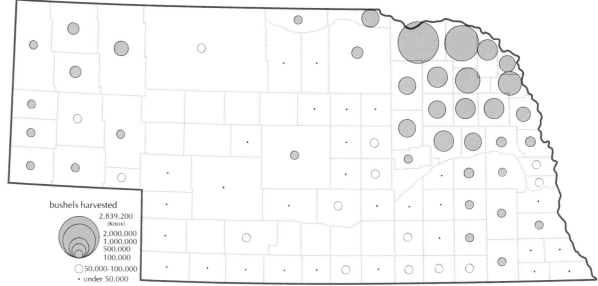

bushels harvested

2,839,200 (Knox)
2,000,000
1,000,000
500,000
100,000
○ 50,000-100,000
· under 50,000

state total: 22,080,000

2–2.5 million acres of the first half of this century to the present half-million mark. For the ten-year period 1965–1974 the harvested oat acreage averaged 526,000 acres, with an average production of 22.7 million bushels. The yield per acre increased steadily during that period, averaging 43.3 bushels (graph 4.7).

Fig. 4.12. OAT PRODUCTION, 1973 (Nebraska State–Federal Division of Agricultural Statistics)

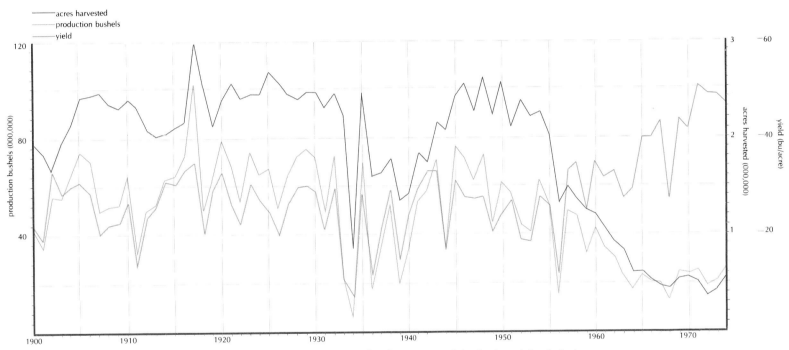

Graph 4.7. OAT TRENDS, 1900–1974 (Nebraska State–Federal Division of Agricultural Statistics)

Barley

Both spring and winter types of barley are produced in Nebraska, although spring barley is confined largely to the northeastern and northwestern areas (figs. 4.13 and 4.14). Spring barley production has declined sharply from the late 1930s and early 1940s, when it was grown extensively because it performed better than wheat under drought conditions (graph 4.8). During the period 1965–74, spring barley production averaged 1.2 million bushels on 35,900 harvested acres, for a 34.3 bushel per acre average. The crop is used as a feed grain.

Winter barley is currently grown on a very small acreage in Nebraska. The inadequate winterhardiness of this fall-seeded crop is its chief drawback, since high-yielding, good-strawed varieties are available. If its winterhardiness can be improved, winter barley acreage may be expected to increase, especially as a dryland feed grain in the southwestern part of the state.

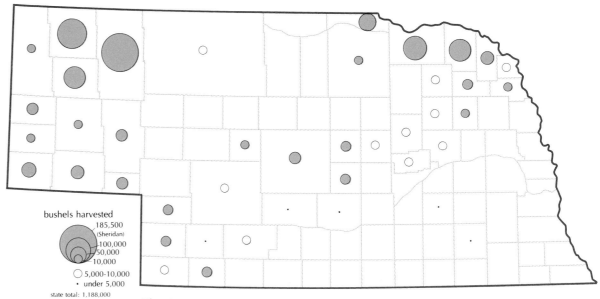

bushels harvested

185,500 (Sheridan)
100,000
50,000
10,000
○ 5,000–10,000
· under 5,000

state total: 1,188,000

Fig. 4.14. BARLEY PRODUCTION, 1973 (Nebraska State–Federal Division of Agricultural Statistics)

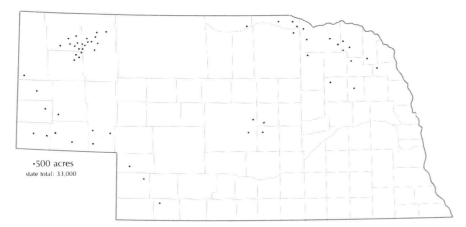

·500 acres
state total: 33,000

Fig. 4.13. BARLEY ACRES HARVESTED, 1973 (Nebraska State–Federal Division of Agricultural Statistics)

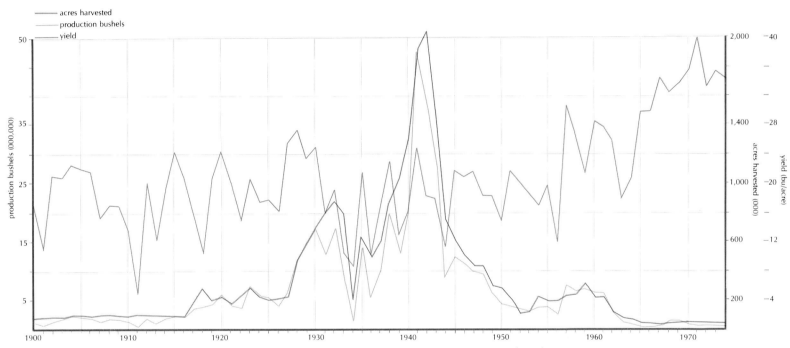

Graph 4.8. BARLEY TRENDS, 1900–1974 (Nebraska State–Federal Division of Agricultural Statistics)

Rye

Rye consistently occupies a restricted but significant place in Nebraska's agriculture. It is grown on the periphery of the Sandhills and on sandy land throughout the state, where its winterhardiness and ability to perform well under poorer soil conditions are important (figs. 4.15 and 4.16). In those areas it may not be harvested for grain because it serves also as a cover crop for the prevention of wind erosion on the light, sandy soils. Rye production has increased during years of adverse weather and decreased during favorable years (graph 4.9).

The growing rye crop may be used for animal pasture in the fall and spring or harvested for grain and used for feed or food. Grain yields of rye have been low in comparison with those of other small-grain crops.

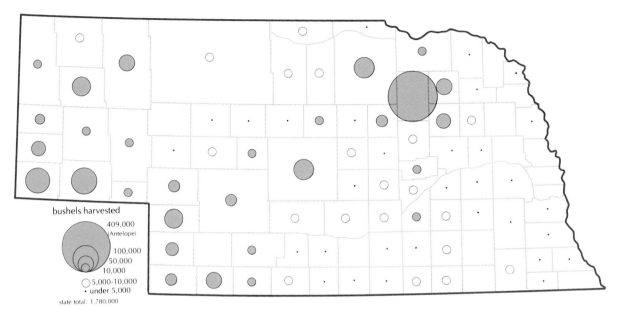

Fig. 4.16. RYE PRODUCTION, 1973 (Nebraska State–Federal Division of Agricultural Statistics)

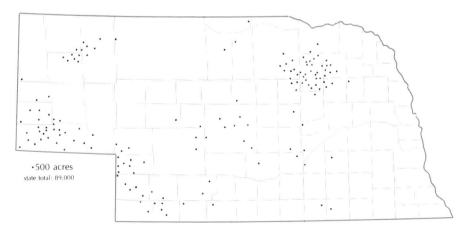

Fig. 4.15. RYE ACRES HARVESTED, 1973 (Nebraska State– Federal Division of Agricultural Statistics)

58

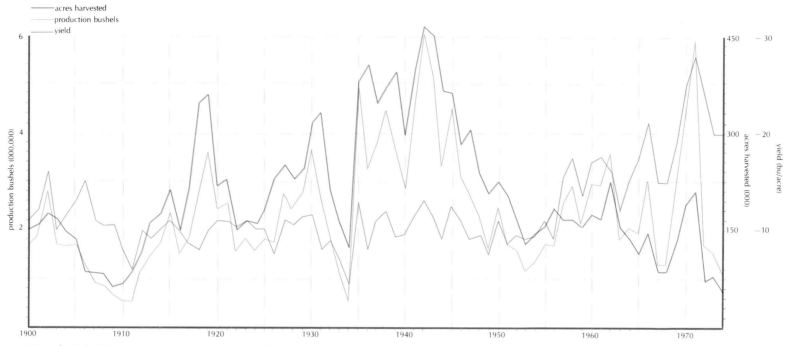

Graph 4.9. RYE TRENDS, 1900–1974 (Nebraska State–Federal Division of Agricultural Statistics)

Millet

Millets have been produced in Nebraska for many years but usually on small acreages. Foxtail-type millets have been grown for forage, and more recently, proso millets have been grown and used for birdseed, feed grain, and forage. Millets are useful for seeding on land where winter wheat has had to be abandoned because of adverse weather. It is a short-season crop and may be planted in late spring to replace a small-grain crop lost to hail.

Proso millets are the predominant type grown, and of these, the white-seeded varieties are the most popular. Over the five-year period 1969–1973, about 50,000 harvested acres of proso millets produced an average of 1,264 pounds per acre.

The millets are specialty crops and their production is influenced by the need for a replacement crop because of either the diversion of other crops in farm programs or crop loss from adverse weather, and by the market demand for special products such as birdseed. However, the development of improved proso-type millets could lead to their establishment as a dependable source of feed grain.

J. W. SCHMIDT

59

FORAGE CROPS AND GRASSLAND

More than one-half of Nebraska's productive land is grasslands, and in addition, many acres of cropland are used to produce forage feeds. The state has more than 24 million acres in pasture and range. Hay is harvested from more than 4 million acres and corn and sorghum silages from 560,000. Crop residues are used from another 4 million acres of land cropped with feed grains and wheat. Of the 49 million acres used for agriculture, nearly 34 million produce forage crops. The feed value of all forage crops grown in the state was estimated at $720 million in 1973 (table 4.1).

The primary forage crops—hay, pasture, and silage—provide almost 80 percent of the total feed budget for beef production, nearly 60 percent for dairy, and nearly 90 percent for sheep. Forage crops grown and fed on farms and ranches rank second, after corn, as the most valuable crop in the state. Because of recent changes in the feeding of beef for slaughter, greater emphasis has been placed upon the need for forage crops.

The Grasslands

Nebraska has about 24 million acres of land in grass, either as pasture or as range. Range lands are often too steep, too dry, too rocky, or too rough to farm. In most cases, pastures are more productive than range and offer other alternatives for crop production. Pastures are often seeded to new grasses and legumes for grazing and can be productive for many years. For example, bromegrass pastures have remained productive without reseeding for more than forty years in some areas of eastern Nebraska.

Seedings of improved varieties of grasses and legumes have been made on more than 1.5 million acres in the state. Pasture seedings are often perennial grasses and legumes planted in mixtures; however, in recent years annuals such as sudangrass and oats, wheat, or rye have been used to seed temporary pastures.

Nearly 1 million acres of relatively poor pastures and range lands need to be reseeded. For reseeding, many types of grasses, legumes, and annual small grains are used. Smooth bromegrass has been the most popular for seeding improved pastures in eastern Nebraska, while the wheatgrasses grow best in the western part of the state. The most common among the cool-season grasses used are smooth bromegrass, intermediate wheatgrass, crested wheatgrass, orchardgrass, reed canarygrass, western wheatgrass, timothy, redtop, and Kentucky bluegrass.

Not all seedings for grassland improvement have been made with cool-season grasses. Warm-season grasses, which grow during the hot summer much as the corn crop does are found in natural prairie regions like the Sandhills. Agricultural scientists have demonstrated the value of reseeding with natural prairie grasses, often called native grasses. These grasses, found in the natural prairie regions, were used in both pasture and range seedings on more than 2 million acres in Nebraska from 1954 to 1974 in conservation programs to control erosion, bring stability to soils susceptible to erosion, and reseed grassland. The grasses most commoly used are big bluestem, Indian grass, switchgrass, side-oats gramma, little bluestem, and sandbluestem.

Table 4.1.

Forage Resource	Average No. Acres	Animal Unit Mos. of Grazing or Equivalent	Estimated Dollar Value
Pasture and Range	24,800,000	19,200,000	$381,000,000
Hay (all kinds)	4,200,000	21,400,000	172,000,000
Corn and Sorghum Silage	560,000	9,270,000	98,500,000
Green Chop Feeds	16,570	78,400	1,466,000
Crop Residues	4,388,000	5,260,000	56,500,000

percentage of
crop irrigated

20%
40%
60%
80%

less than 1% not indicated

tons harvested

332,000
(Dawson)
200,000
100,000
50,000
15,000
· under 15,000

state total: 7,155,000

Fig. 4.17. CORN SILAGE PRODUCTION, 1972 (Nebraska State–Federal Division of Agricultural Statistics)

The Silage Crops

Corn and sorghum are the principal crops harvested for silage, but others such as oats, rye, wheat, and alfalfa are also used. Ensilage preserves the feed value for months and even years when the crops are stored in sound structures. The gradual but steady increase in the total tonnage harvested for silage has parallelled the growth in feeder cattle and background feeding operations (figs. 4.17 and 4.18; graph 4.10).

A major portion of the crop harvested for silage is irrigated. More than 67 percent of the acreage of corn harvested as silage in 1973 was irrigated, and it produced more than 80 percent of the silage corn.

Although the acreage of sorghum harvested for silage has declined since 1966, when more than 1.9 million tons were harvested, this crop continues to provide many tons of feed (graph 4.11). The primary area for growing sorghum for silage is in the southern part of the state, where lack of rainfall restricts the growing of corn for silage unless irrigated.

61

Cutting corn for silage, one of the major forage crops in Nebraska.

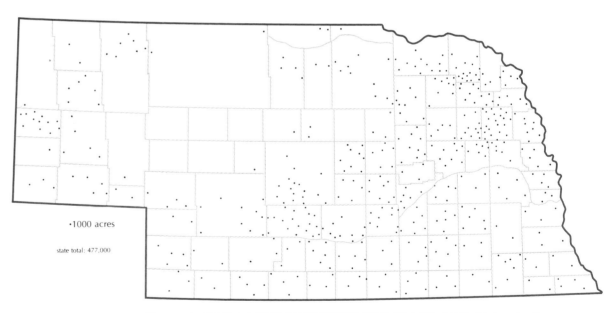

•1000 acres

state total: 477,000

Fig. 4.18. CORN ACRES HARVESTED FOR SILAGE, 1972 (Nebraska State–Federal Division of Agricultural Statistics)

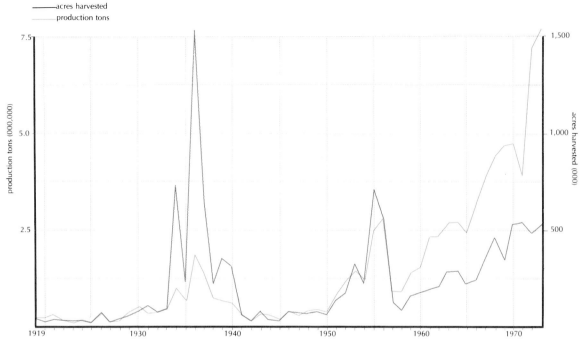

Graph 4.10. CORN SILAGE TRENDS, 1919–73 (Nebraska State–Federal Division of Agricultural Statistics)

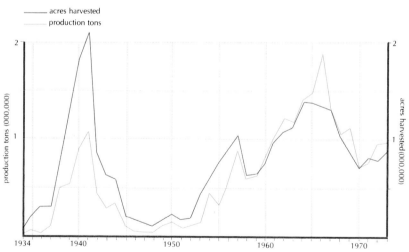

Graph 4.11. SORGHUM SILAGE TRENDS, 1934–73 (Nebraska State–Federal Division of Agricultural Statistics)

63

The Hay Crops

Hay is a valuable commodity in Nebraska, ranking near wheat in value. The crops, which are harvested from fertile farm lands that have been seeded to improved grasses and legumes, are an important source of winter feed for beef cattle. Many of the 2.1 million acres of wild hay found in the sub-irrigated meadows have been improved through overseeding with timothy, redtop and clovers (figs. 4.19 and 4.20). Upland wild hay is often harvested from the more productive range lands that are too hilly and too dry for farming (fig. 4.21). Cut on an alternating yearly basis, it is harvested only once in every two or three years on these lands.

Many natural grasses, legumes, sedges, and forbs called wild hay do not produce adequate yields. Because of the potential for better profits on land that is not too steep, too rocky, or too wet, many farmers and ranchers reseed poorly producing wild hay-lands to better hay-producing varieties of grasses and legumes.

Alfalfa, the major forage legume in Nebraska, has been harvested from more than 1.4 million acres of productive agricultural land (figs. 4.22 and 4.23). Other legumes that are often grown for hay are red clover, white clover, and, to some degree, sweet clover. These legumes are important because they produce their own nitrogen and

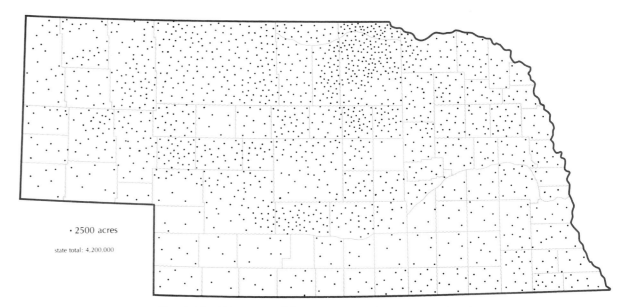

· 2500 acres

state total: 4,200,000

Fig. 4.19. ALL HAY ACRES HARVESTED, 1973 (Nebraska State–Federal Division of Agricultural Statistics)

Baling hay. Large bales provide an efficient means of storing quality hay for livestock.

64

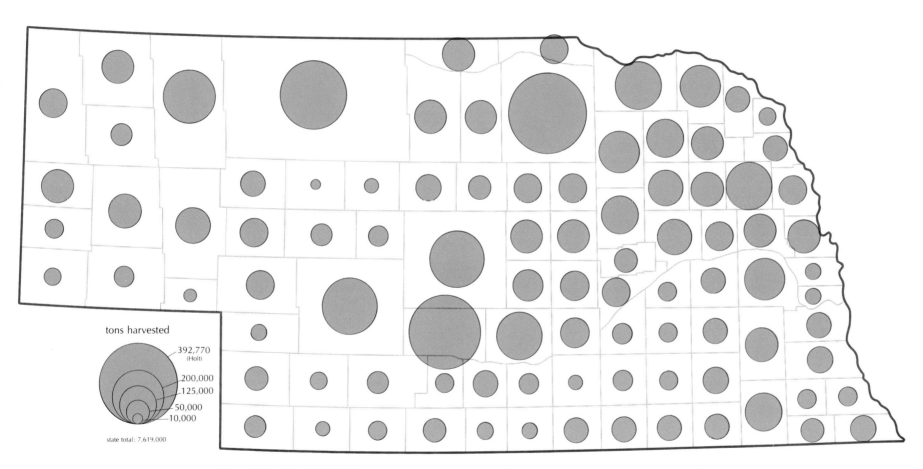

tons harvested

392,770
(Holt)

200,000
125,000

50,000
10,000

state total: 7,619,000

Fig. 4.20. ALL HAY PRODUCTION, 1973 (Nebraska State–Federal Division of Agricultural Statistics)

are a highly productive source of feed protein.

The tall-growing perennial cool-season and warm-season grasses are also grown and cut for hay. Smooth bromegrass, orchardgrass, wheatgrass, timothy, and redtop are the principal hay-producing grasses that grow during spring and early summer. Common warm-season grasses used for hay are big bluestem, indiangrass, and side-oats gramma. Annuals such as sudangrass, sorghum-sudangrass crosses, and hybrid sorghums, often called cane hay, are planted by ranchers in the southwestern counties for annual hay crops.

Crop Residues

Crop residues are the parts of the plants left after the grain harvest. Although the idea of using them for feed is not new, the recent emphasis on beef production and the resulting demands for feed have made these crops more important. In counties of high beef cattle numbers, corn and sorghum farmers make moderate to heavy use of the residues; only in the eastern and southeastern cropping districts have they been used sparingly.

Alfalfa Dehydration

Nebraska produces about 45 percent of the national total of "dehy"—hay that is dehydrated to preserve its nutritional value—principally from alfalfa. The crop from nearly 27 percent of the alfalfa acreage in Ne-

66

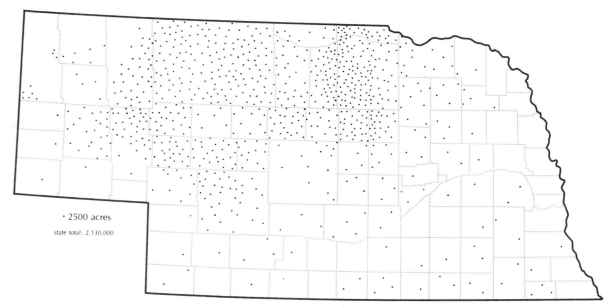

· 2500 acres

state total: 2,130,000

Fig. 4.21. WILD HAY ACRES HARVESTED, 1973 (Nebraska State–Federal Division of Agricultural Statistics)

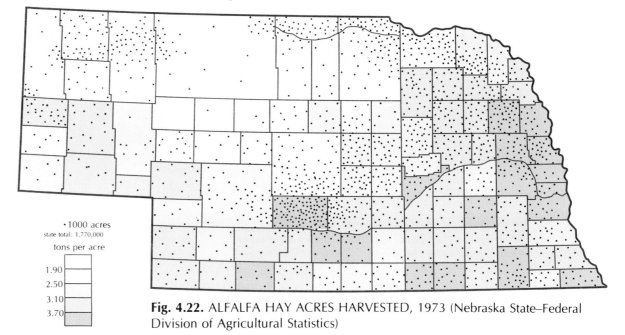

· 1000 acres

state total: 1,770,000

tons per acre

1.90	
2.50	
3.10	
3.70	

Fig. 4.22. ALFALFA HAY ACRES HARVESTED, 1973 (Nebraska State–Federal Division of Agricultural Statistics)

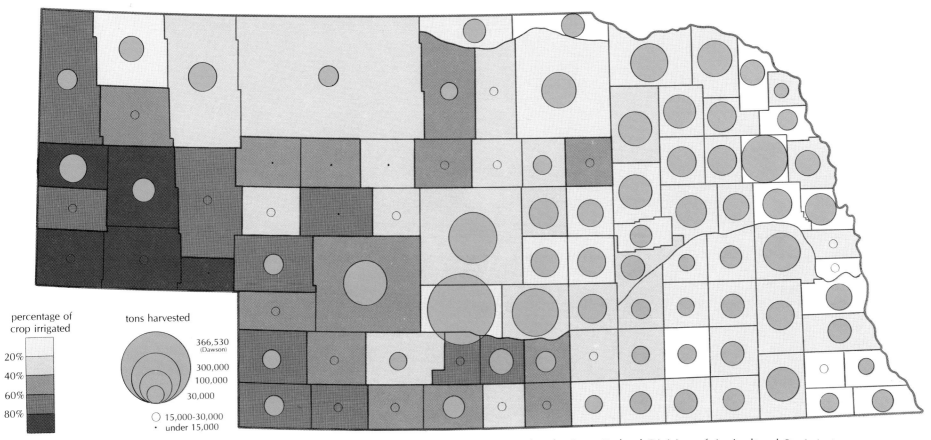

Fig. 4.23. ALFALFA HAY PRODUCTION, 1973 (Nebraska State–Federal Division of Agricultural Statistics)

braska is processed into "dehy." Alfalfa meal, an important ingredient in livestock rations, and an excellent source of protein, vitamins, and minerals, is purchased by large commercial livestock enterprises that formulate their own rations and by commercial feed manufacturers. The cost of transporting freshly cut alfalfa from the field to the dehydration plant requires that plants be located in the immediate production area. As a result, most dehydration facilities are found along the Platte River valley, with the greatest concentration in Dawson County. The number of plants remained nearly constant from 1950 to 1960 but increased sharply from 55 in 1960 to 81 by the end of 1973, when the industry had a combined total of 154 dehydration drums. The annual production per drum varies from 3,000 to 12,000 tons.

WALLY J. MOLINE

SUGAR BEETS

Sugar beets are the most important cash crop on irrigated cropland in western Nebraska. The acreage has gradually increased since the 1950s, when production became more mechanized (graph 4.12). The acreage has exceeded 70,000 acres since 1968, with a high of 87,300 in 1969. Yields per acre have varied greatly from year to year but have gradually increased. The highest average tonnage was 20.1 tons per acre in 1972. In 1973 Nebraska ranked seventh in the nation in sugar beet production, with 6.3 percent of the acreage.

Sugar beets at one time were grown in three areas: in the northeast near Sioux City; in the general triangle formed by Grand Island, Holdrege, and Hastings in central Nebraska; and in the North and South Platte valleys in the western part of the state. Today, most of the crop is produced in western Nebraska (figs. 4.24 and 4.25).

Sugar beets are well adapted to the alkaline soils found in the western counties. The crop has a relatively small seed and sometimes is difficult to establish. Once established, however, the hardy plants will survive many disasters such as insect damage and hailstorms that destroy other crops. Since the sugar beet is a root crop, destroying the leaves only delays the growth period during the summer.

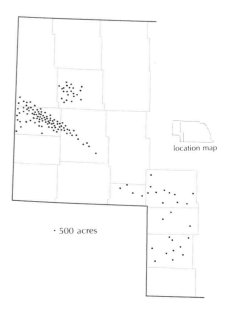

location map

· 500 acres

Fig. 4.24. SUGAR BEET ACRES HARVESTED, 1973 (Nebraska State–Federal Division of Agricultural Statistics)

Graph 4.12. SUGAR BEET TRENDS, 1924–74 (Nebraska State–Federal Division of Agricultural Statistics)

Much manual labor was needed in the past to establish the crop and to harvest the roots. A thick stand had to be planted because not all the seeds would germinate and develop. If germination was good, stands had to be thinned and the small plants and weeds removed by hand hoeing. Before 1950, the crop was harvested by hand, primarily by migrant workers brought into the state from the South and from Mexico. In the 1950s and 1960s, machines were developed which would separate the top from the root, dig the root, and place it into a bin, eliminating much of the hand work at a time when migrant labor was becoming scarce. It was also during the 1960s that herbicides were developed, further reducing the hand labor needed. These developments drastically changed farming practices for sugar beets and enabled an individual farmer to grow a crop without depending heavily on hand labor.

Sugar beets are usually planted the first two weeks in April, in narrow rows twenty-two inches wide. The small seedlings emerge in five to ten days and can withstand temperatures down to 24°F. Spring rainfall is usually adequate for growth of the small plants and irrigation is not started until July. All sugar beets are produced under irrigation, which is essential for a good yield. The cold-hardy beets are harvested in October, using a growing season of from 120 to 150 days. The average production of 20 tons of beets per acre obtained in some years represents over 65 one-hundred-pound bags of pure white sugar for each acre. On exceptional farms 100 bags of sugar per acre have been produced. There are four sugar factories in operation in Nebraska, all in Scotts Bluff County.

FRANK N. ANDERSON

Custer 600 tons
Dawson 33,810 tons
Gosper 3,610 tons
Kearney 3,460 tons
Lincoln 24,620 tons
Red Willow 7,550 tons

location map

production tons

678,520
(Scotts Bluff)

200,000

75,000

25,000

10,000

Fig. 4.25. SUGAR BEET PRODUCTION, 1973 (Nebraska State–Federal Division of Agricultural Statistics)

An elevator stands guard over a mountain of sugar beets awaiting processing.

DRY EDIBLE BEANS

Dry edible beans were first introduced into the state in the 1920s by a Nebraskan who saw them growing in Idaho under conditions similar to those in western Nebraska. By 1928, a small bean-processing plant was established at Morrill. In the years that followed, beans were produced, mainly under furrow irrigation, in all the western counties (figs. 4.26 and 4.27).

Most of the crop is produced in Scotts Bluff, Box Butte, and Morrill Counties. Before the early 1950s, dry beans were grown on very little acreage outside the western counties of the Panhandle. Since then a considerable acreage, mostly under sprinkler irrigation, has been in production in Deuel, Keith, Perkins, and Chase Counties. The acreage, about 72,000 acres, changed little from 1964 to 1967 (graph 4.13), but a sharp increase occurred in 1968 and a record high of 113,000 harvested acres was reached in 1974. Great Northern beans are grown on 65–80 percent of the acreage and pinto beans on the remainder, except for about 1,000 acres of California pink beans.

Nebraska has ranked first in Great Northern bean and third in pinto bean production for many years and stands fifth in total production of dry edible beans. The average yield remained between 1,800 and 2,000 pounds per acre from 1966 to 1974 (graph 4.13). Yields of 40–45 bushels per acre are obtained under irrigation, with good man-

agement. An average yield of 6.4 bushels per acre has been obtained on the limited acreage of dryland beans.

Self-propelled, pick-up combines are used to thresh the crop. The beans are transported in bulk to the local warehouse or elevator, where they are graded for quality and tare and processed for sale. Screen-air separators and electric-eye sorting machines are used in the cleaning process. On occasion, some lots of beans are hand-picked.

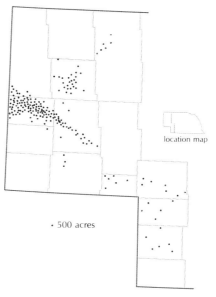

Fig. 4.26. DRY EDIBLE BEAN ACRES HARVESTED, 1973 (Nebraska State–Federal Division of Agricultural Statistics)

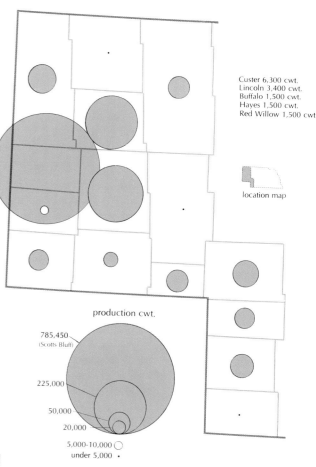

Custer 6,300 cwt.
Lincoln 3,400 cwt.
Buffalo 1,500 cwt.
Hayes 1,500 cwt.
Red Willow 1,500 cwt.

Fig. 4.27. DRY EDIBLE BEAN PRODUCTION, 1973 (Nebraska State–Federal Division of Agricultural Statistics)

Great Northern beans are sold mainly in the dry package trade, while pinto beans are used both in that trade and in canning. Great Northern beans do not have good canning qualities but are desirable for use in baked beans and soups. An excellent source of cheap protein, beans contain about 20–23 percent protein.

D. P. COYNE

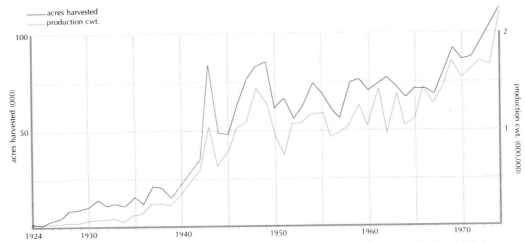

Graph 4.13. DRY EDIBLE BEAN TRENDS, 1924–74 (Nebraska State–Federal Division of Agricultural Statistics)

One of many bean fields in western Nebraska ditched for irrigation.

POTATOES

Potatoes are grown as a late summer crop in central and eastern Nebraska and as a fall crop in the Panhandle (fig. 4.28). Production has declined since 1949 (graph 4.14). The maximum acreage of 70,000 acres was raised during World War II but only 10,000 acres were grown in 1970.

The acreage fluctuates in producing counties, but new areas have come into production since 1960 because of a demand for processing potatoes. Trends in acreage, yields, and production in Nebraska are comparable to national trends. A reduction in acreage but much higher production per acre have been accompanied by a reduction in numbers of growers but larger acreage per grower. In 1970, 89 percent as many potatoes were produced as in 1936 on 15 percent as many acres. The acreage and production have shifted from dryland to irrigated cropland since 1955. In the past, potatoes were generally furrow irrigated; now, 85 percent of the acreage is sprinkler irrigated, generally with the center-pivot type of system.

Changes have occurred in the use of potatoes. Approximately 70 percent of the present-day crop is being used by potato chip and frozen and dehydrated product processors, 8 percent as fresh table potatoes, and 22 percent for export seed. By comparison, in 1955, 25 percent of the crop was

Graph 4.14. POTATO TRENDS (Nebraska State–Federal Division of Agricultural Statistics)

exported as seed potatoes and the remainder was sold as fresh table potatoes. Again, these changes in production and use of Nebraska potatoes are consistent with those occurring nationally.

Shifts to production with center-pivot sprinkler irrigation, the complete mechanization of all cultivation and harvest operations, and modern controlled-environment storage have accompanied the transition to the production of processing potatoes. Three

companies in Omaha, one in Lincoln, and one in Scottsbluff produce and distribute potato chips. One Omaha company uses potatoes in frozen dinners.

From 1965 to 1970 net returns to the grower averaged from $50 to $125 per acre, depending on the year and type of potatoes produced; net returns ranged from $275 to $590 per acre in 1973. The average prices paid to growers from 1965 to 1970 were $1.74 and $1.58 per hundredweight for

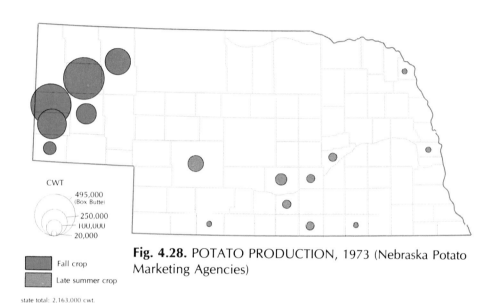

CWT
495,000 (Box Butte)
250,000
100,000
20,000

Fall crop

Late summer crop

state total: 2,163,000 cwt.

Fig. 4.28. POTATO PRODUCTION, 1973 (Nebraska Potato Marketing Agencies)

HORTICULTURAL CROPS

Horticulture plays an important part in the way of life of Nebraska's citizens and contributes significantly to the economy. It enhances the quality of life through improved diet, attractively designed landscapes, and recreational opportunities in parks, gardens, and golf courses. Home gardening provides a hobby, recreation, means of artistic expression, attractive landscapes, and fresh, nutritious fruits and vegetables for the family. Plants are used to brighten business, shopping, and residential areas, and along highways to reduce the hazards of snowdrifts and for noise abatement. In recent years there has been an increased interest in growing all kinds of horticultural plants. The total annual value of the ornamental plant and turf industries and home horticulture to Nebraska is $159.7 million, not including parks, public grounds, cemeteries, landscape and maintenance services, and some plant and maintenance items.

The established commercial vegetable crops are dry beans, potatoes, cucumbers, onions, greenhouse and field tomatoes, and small acreages of other assorted fresh vegetable crops including melons, squash, and sweet corn. Nearly 600 acres of pickling cucumbers are produced in the northeastern and southeastern parts of the state. Melons and squash are raised on 900 acres, primarily in the Loup River valley. Approxi-

chipping and table-stock potatoes, respectively. The comparable prices paid to growers in 1973 were $2.50 and $3.95.

Contract production of potatoes has developed along with the production of processing potatoes since 1960. Contract prices for the 1974 crop ranged from $2.25 to $3.00 per hundredweight.

The demand for chipping potatoes is increasing at the rate of about 3 percent per year. Two firms have been established in eastern Nebraska that specialize in the production and packaging of fresh table potatoes, and 600 additional acres were grown in 1974 for that purpose.

R. B. O'KEEFE

mately 300 acres of onions are produced, principally in western Nebraska, although the production of onions for frozen-onion-ring processing is developing on small acreages in the central and eastern areas. Onion rings are processed in Grand Island and Wahoo. Greenhouse tomato production has developed since 1963 to satisfy part of the demand for out-of-season tomatoes. There are at present 28 greenhouse tomato–growing operations located in Nebraska. The 1970 value of vegetable production and imports in Nebraska was $27.6 million.

Modern fruit-producing enterprises are located in the Missouri River Valley, and there are, in addition, a few small operations in the south-central and eastern counties. In 1970 approximately 40 growers produced 700 acres of fruit. Apples at a value of $420,000 accounted for 560 acres; cherries with a value of $84,000 were grown on 70 acres; and peaches with a value of $12,000 were produced on 35 acres. Plums and grapes were produced on 35 acres or more.

Trees and forest products contribute much to the state's economy. Trees are also valuable in enhancing the beauty of the environment and in providing protection for wildlife and crops. Two percent, or one million acres, of privately owned land in Nebraska is in forest. Approximately 25,000 Christmas trees at a value of 175,000 dollars are produced and marketed in the state annually. They are grown on 400 acres by 45 growers. Windbreaks for crop and livestock protection extend for a total of 20,000 miles and cover 160,000 acres. Approximately 40 million board feet of lumber, of which 3.0

million are walnut, are cut annually and are valued at $2.0 million. In addition, 2.3 million trees are distributed and planted annually in Nebraska through the cooperative state and federal Clark-McNary tree-distribution program.

D. P. COYNE
R. B. O'KEEFE

SEED PRODUCTION

The professionally oriented seed industry is relatively new to agriculture. For generations, farmers saved grain from the year's harvest to plant their next crop. Then, in the early 1900s, they became more concerned about the quality of the seed they planted. With increased interest in crop performance came research and breeding programs to develop improved varieties, and the seed industry evolved to produce and distribute these new varieties, which are the heart of any successful cropping system.

Over the years, Nebraska has gained recognition as a leading state in diversified seed production. A number of factors have contributed to its status.

Both the University of Nebraska and commercial seed companies have had excellent programs for the development of new crop varieties. These new varieties require careful handling to protect their identity. Through the Foundation Seed Division of the University of Nebraska's Department of Agronomy

and the seed certification program of the Nebraska Crop Improvement Association, seeds of new varieties have been made available to qualified growers. This has encouraged Nebraska seed producers to develop their expertise and seed-production facilities. Moreover, the high quality of farm operations in the state is a particular asset in seed production. These invaluable resources of production knowhow have attracted many seed companies to produce in Nebraska and provided them with a stable source of high-quality seed.

Nebraska has a variety of fertile, productive soil types—light, medium, and heavy soils—with topography from level to rolling, which offer a range of sites well suited to the production of a variety of crop seeds. The growing season is generally conducive to crop production, normally providing adequate rainfall for good yields and dry fall weather enabling the harvest of good-quality seed. The large acreage under irrigation and vast supply of underground water provide insurance against drought and a dependable environment for seed production. Finally, the state's easy accessibility is invaluable in facilitating seed distribution to the major agricultural production areas of the United States.

Corn

Nebraska contributed much to the earliest work on hybrid corn through the state experiment station and private companies. Its climate is ideal for the production of hybrid seed corn, although occasional droughts are

74

a drawback. These are being overcome by increased irrigation in areas of the best corn-growing soils. Seed industry surveys indicate that production of hybrid seed corn increased more than five times in both acreage and yield in the period 1954–74.

Sorghum

The development of hybrid sorghums in the mid-1950s produced a big demand for seed of both grain and forage sorghums. Seed production in Nebraska rose steadily for several years, but the poor quality resulting from early frosts has forced seed companies to shift their production southward. Although frost does not pose a threat in the normal development of this important crop, seed production employs the use of longer-season seed parents, and early frost becomes a problem in some years. When seed technology overcomes this problem, the state will recover a significant position in the production of hybrid sorghum seed.

Wheat

Wheat has been an important crop in Nebraska since the state was settled. New and improved wheat varieties released in Nebraska have produced a steady demand for seed. Farmers are becoming more and more aware of the advantages of seed wheat produced by specialized growers. The amount of wheat produced specifically for seed increased threefold in the years from 1954 to 1974.

The development of hybrid wheats may further increase Nebraska's desirability for seed wheat production, particularly where center-pivot irrigation is available. With irrigation as insurance against loss due to drought, the higher value of hybrid seed wheat should attract new growers.

Soybeans

As the popularity of soybeans has increased in the state, seed producers have increased

their production to meet the larger demand. Between 1954 and 1974 the planted acreage of soybeans increased nearly sevenfold. Certified soybean seed production kept pace with that trend, increasing over sixfold. In addition, private companies greatly increased the production of soybean seed in the latter half of that period.

Grasses

Nebraska has been a grass seed producer for many years. Introduced grasses, such as bromegrass and wheatgrasses, have been produced extensively in the state. Comparatively recently, the pioneering work of Nebraska grass breeders with warm-season grasses has led to an expanded production capacity and greater demand for the seed of these grasses.

Detasseled seed rows and pollination rows in a hybrid corn seed production field.

Oats

In 1954, nearly 20,000 acres of oats were certified in Nebraska, but since then certified seed oats production has declined. Commercial and seed oats production is very sensitive to government acreage controls. When government regulations became more restrictive in the 1960s, seed oat acreages fell drastically, hitting a low of 1,000 acres or less in 1964 and 1972. In the mid-1970s, when government restrictions were eased, oat acreages, both seed and commercial, increased significantly.

Dry Beans

Nebraska has led in the development of new, improved varieties of dry edible beans since 1960. As dry bean production increased, farmers in the western part of the state demanded greater quantities of locally produced seed. The possibilities for future growth in dry bean seed production are bright as newer varieties are developed.

Other Crops

Nebraska also produces seed for other crops, such as potatoes, alfalfa, sweet clover, millet, barley, and rye. In 1973, 22 percent of the potato crop was exported for seed, and legume seed (alfalfa, red clover, and hairy vetch) was harvested on 32,000 acres. Seed of just about any adapted crop can be produced economically in the state.

DEAN LANCASTER

5
Animal Production

Nebraska is a leader in livestock production, an enterprise that has been important to its economy ever since the state was settled. In recent years, livestock production has contributed more than one-half the cash farm receipts (fig. 5.1) and cash receipts have been increasing in both total and real value (graph 5.1). Nearly half the businesses and firms in Nebraska—including ones as diverse as banks, insurance firms, auto service agencies, and grocery stores—depend on animal agriculture for a market, a raw material, or a service opportunity.

Nebraska has feed resources for a sound, expanding animal agriculture, which in turn increases the value of that basic resource and contributes to the economic growth of the state. In the United States, per capita meat consumption rose 42 pounds, from 145 to 187 pounds—a 29 percent increase—between 1950 and 1974. This trend is expected to continue both in the United States and worldwide.

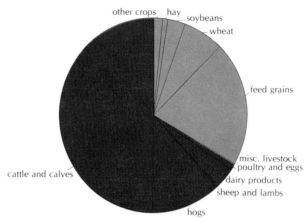

Fig. 5.1. CASH RECEIPTS FOR CROPS AND LIVESTOCK 1969–73 Average Nebraska State–Federal Division of Agricultural Statistics)

Cattle converting Sandhills grass into quality food for humans.

78

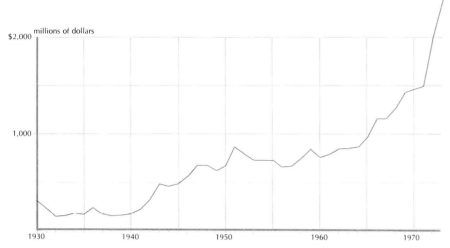

$2,000 | millions of dollars

1,000

1930   1940   1950   1960   1970

Graph 5.1. RECEIPTS FROM LIVESTOCK MARKETINGS, 1930–73 (Nebraska State–Federal Division of Agricultural Statistics)

CATTLE

In 1867, when Nebraska became the thirty-seventh state, there were 115,000 head of cattle within its boundaries. One hundred seven years later—in 1974–the number stood at 7,410,000 head and the cattle industry constituted the most important segment of the state's economy.

The first cattle to graze within the bounds of present-day Nebraska belonged to the soldiers at Fort Atkinson in the early 1820s. Through the mid-1800s, cattle raising had

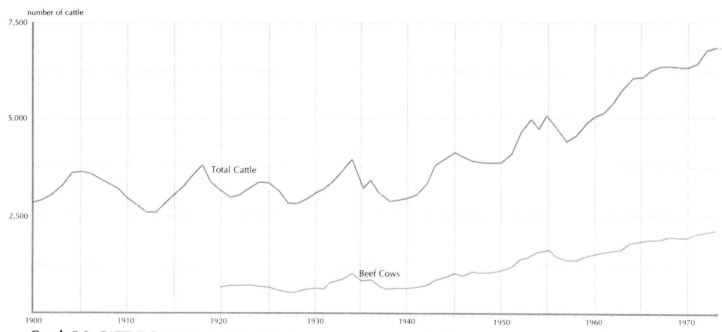

number of cattle

7,500

Total Cattle

5,000

2,500

Beef Cows

1900   1910   1920   1930   1940   1950   1960   1970

Graph 5.2. CATTLE ON FARMS, 1900–1973 (Nebraska State–Federal Division of Agricultural Statistics)

some influence on the state's economy; then, in 1879, the discovery of the productiveness of the Sandhills region paved the way for the full-scale development of the cattle industry.

Nebraska is well adapted for cattle production as a result of a fortunate combination of water resources, forage and feed grain production, and geographic location. Cattle raising has increased substantially since the drought of the 1930s (graph 5.2) and is now important to the economy of every county (fig. 5.2). The annual marketings of Nebraska cattle totaled more than $2 billion, in 1974, making the state one of the top in the nation in cattle production. It ranks first in carcass beef production, second in fed cattle marketing, third in all cattle inventory, fourth in calves born, and in cash receipts from cattle and calves.

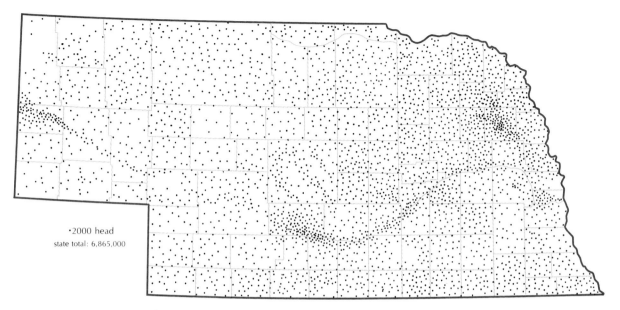

·2000 head
state total: 6,865,000

Fig. 5.2. CATTLE ON FARMS, January 1, 1973 (Nebraska State–Federal Division of Agricultural Statistics)

Beef Cattle

Beef cow numbers tripled in Nebraska between 1940 and 1974. Increases during the 1940s and 1950s resulted largely from range improvement and replacement of dairy herds, while those in the 1960s were brought about by improved utilization of range and an increasing supply of crop residues.

On the average, Nebraska livestock producers convert only 60 percent of the feed grains raised in the state into livestock. The total supply could sustain nearly twice the number of livestock currently produced. Improved technology, coupled with further expansion in irrigation, will result in further increases in feed grain production. This potential increased supply of feed grains and associated crop residues will stimulate the expansion of cow herds, particularly in the farming areas of the state.

Calf Production

Nebraska is one of the leading states in the number of calves raised, ranking fourth. Approximately half the calves are raised in the range areas of the Panhandle, the Sandhills, and the southwest; the remainder come from the more traditional farming areas.

Ranches, some covering 50,000 acres or more, dominate calf production. The selection of bulls, culling of herds, and other

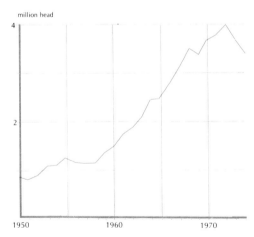

million head

Graph 5.3. FED CATTLE MARKETED, 1950–73 (Nebraska State–Federal Division of Agricultural Statistics)

ranch activities require long hours and good management to produce a top-quality end product. Generally feeder calves or yearlings are the rancher's contribution to the meat industry.

Cattle Feeding

Cattle feeding has become a major industry in Nebraska. During the 1960s and early 1970s it was a particularly fast-growing enterprise, with a rate of growth nearly double the national rate (graph 5.3). Moreover, continued expansion in the industry is expected to center on Nebraska because of its centralized location and natural resources.

Although the state has commercial feedlots that range up to 40,000 head in capacity, the farmer-feeder plays an important role in the feeding industry. Nebraska has over 14,000 lots with fewer than 1,000 head of cattle on feed. In most such enterprises cattle feeding complements the farming operation. The trend, however, is toward larger feedlots. In 1974, over 60 percent of the fed cattle marketed for slaughter came from lots with a capacity of 1,000 head or more. Nebraska has more lots of this size than any other state in the nation.

Even though Nebraska is a leader in feeder cattle production, the output has not kept pace with the needs of the industry. Today the state imports approximately half of its feeder cattle. In the early 1970s, when cattle feeding was at its peak, more feeder cattle were imported than were produced within the state.

Nebraska's climate is suitable for cattle feeding. In eastern areas rainfall is higher than desirable for feeding, but with proper lot design, difficulties with mud are minimal. Heat is a problem for only a few days each summer and is not serious enough to require the use of shades. Cattle feeding tends to be concentrated in the eastern part of the state, the North Platte valley, and irrigated areas of the Panhandle, where there is a long history of feed grain production (fig. 5.3). The increase in cattle feeding has not kept pace, however, with feed grain production in newly irrigated areas; consequently, there is the potential for continued growth in the industry in Nebraska.

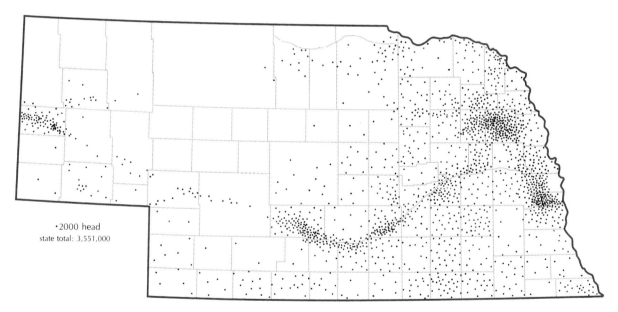

- 2000 head
state total: 3,551,000

Fig. 5.3. CATTLE PLACED ON FEED, 1973 (Nebraska State–Federal Division of Agricultural Statistics)

Beef Cattle Improvement

Nebraska has traditionally produced large numbers of feeder cattle, both calves and yearlings. The selection of bulls to sire these calves has been given high priority by commercial cattlemen, and in recent years increasing attention has been paid to their selection on the basis of performance information. Improvement is sought in weaning weight, yearling weight, feed conversion efficiency, and carcass cutability without the sacrifice of fertility, calving ease, and carcass quality (marbling).

Such improvement through genetics is painstakingly slow but economically sound. Nebraska cattlemen have more tools to accomplish it today than they have had in the past. There are two central bull-testing stations sponsored by the Nebraska Beef Cattle Improvement Association and five individual breed association test stations in the state with a combined capacity of 1,000–1,200 bulls. These stations measure a limited set of traits (average daily gain, weight per day of age, and yearling weight) in bulls from eight to thirteen months of age.

While the test stations are used by approximately 160 breeders each year, the majority of performance information comes from on-the-farm or -ranch performance-recording programs. All major beef breed associations now have performance-recording programs available to their members, and most of them also have national sire evaluation programs in various stages of development. Nebraska breeders are taking advantage of these programs in increasing numbers. While purebred cattle make up only 2 percent of the state's total cattle inventory, most commercial cattlemen buy purebred bulls; thus the breeder of registered cattle has a great responsibility to produce superior seedstock. Two national breed associations—the American Shorthorn Association and the Red Poll Cattle Club of America—have headquarters in Nebraska.

Nebraska breeders have also taken advantage of artificial insemination as a tool to achieve greater selection intensity in their bulls. The advantages of crossbreeding have not been readily accepted in the state, but an increasing number of commercial cattlemen have recognized its value and are using it today.

PAUL Q. GUYER

DAIRY CATTLE

Nebraska ranks twenty-third among the states in milk production, with an annual production of approximately 1.4 billion pounds. The major markets for milk are in

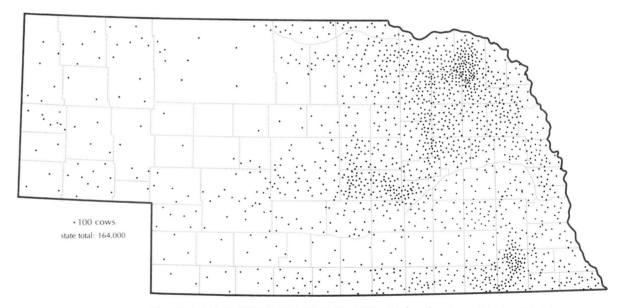

· 100 cows
state total: 164,000

Fig. 5.4. MILK COWS ON FARMS, 1973 (Nebraska State–Federal Division of Agricultural Statistics)

milk cows
milk production
milk lbs./cow

milk production (000,000 lbs.)

3,000

2,000

1,000

milk cows (000)

800

560

400

240

80

milk lbs./cow

—9,000

—6,000

—3,000

1929   1940   1950   1960   1970

Graph 5.4. MILK TRENDS, 1929–73 (Nebraska State–Federal Division of Agricultural Statistics)

The decrease in number of dairy cows was accompanied by a significant reduction in the number of small herds (less than 10 cows). The number of herds of 50–100 cows increased from 279 to 369 during the period 1954–69, and the number of herds of 100 cows or more increased from 23 to 50, indicating a significant trend toward larger commercial operations.

Large capital investments in buildings and equipment to meet Grade A and Environmental Protection Agency regulations has encouraged specialization in dairy farming. In general, owners of large herds have been leaders in the adoption of improved practices in feeding, breeding, and management to achieve more efficient milk production.

P. H. COLE

the Omaha, Lincoln, and Grand Island areas, and more than half of it is produced in the eastern third of the state (fig. 5.4).

Milk and milk products sales rank fourth among farm products in their contribution to the total farm cash receipts. Approximately 4 percent of the state's farm income is derived from the sale of milk and milk products. The disposition of milk from Nebraska farms has changed greatly in recent years. In 1945 less than 12 percent of the milk production was marketed as whole

milk; currently, 90 percent is so marketed. The sale of cream has declined markedly in recent years.

There has been a constant decrease in dairy cow numbers since 1950 (graph 5.4): from 493,000 in that year to 356,000 in 1960 and 158,000 in 1974. At the same time, however, production per cow increased from 4,870 pounds in 1950 to 6,140 pounds in 1960 to 9,476 pounds in 1974, so that total milk production dropped at a relatively slow rate.

Improved breeding and management has nearly doubled the amount of milk produced per cow since 1950.

SWINE

Historically, pork production has been a profitable side business on many Nebraska farms and has long been a significant part of the state's agriculture. Its contribution to farm cash receipts ranged from 30 percent in the 1920s down to about 14 percent in the late 1960s. The pork industry has also played an important role in providing off-farm jobs in the animal health, feed, transportation, marketing, financial, and packing enterprises.

Pork production has been concentrated in the general farm area of the northeast but in recent years has increased in the heavy corn-producing areas of the state and in areas of new irrigation development (fig. 5.5). The shift in production to the nontraditional areas has not been large but has been steady and is expected to continue because of the expanded grain production in areas of intensive irrigation.

Nebraska is one of the major pork-producing states, ranking sixth in the nation in the number of sows farrowed and pigs saved. Between the early 1960s and the mid-1970s, the state's share of the national pig crop increased from 4.5 to 5.5 percent. During that same period the number of farms producing pigs declined from more than 50,000 to less than 30,000. While this resulted in the doubling of the size of the average pork-producing enterprise, fewer than 200 pigs are marketed per farm raising pigs.

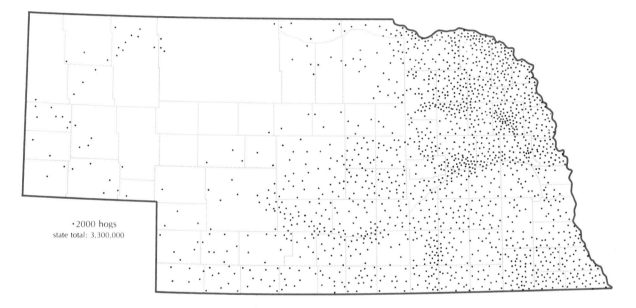

· 2000 hogs
state total: 3,300,000

Fig. 5.5. HOGS ON FARMS, December 1, 1972 (Nebraska State–Federal Division of Agricultural Statistics)

number of swine (000)

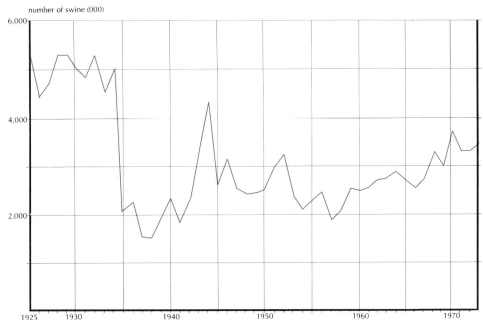

Graph 5.5. HOGS ON FARM, 1925–73 (Nebraska State–Federal Division of Agricultural Statistics)

Intensification of pork production has led to an increase in confinement raising of pigs.

The number of large pork enterprises has increased; in 1974 more than 200 hog farms had inventories of 1,000 head or more. The dominant factor in the increase has been the development in the 1970s of large feeder-pig corporations, which produce from 7,000 to 15,000 pigs per year and are generally owned by small groups of farmers who buy feeder pigs. At the end of 1974, these corporations accounted for about 7 percent of Nebraska's sow inventory and were producing 8–10 percent of the state's pig crop. Modern management systems allow such units to produce more pigs than the sow numbers might indicate.

Pork production is flexible enough to help the farmer cope with changing times. The

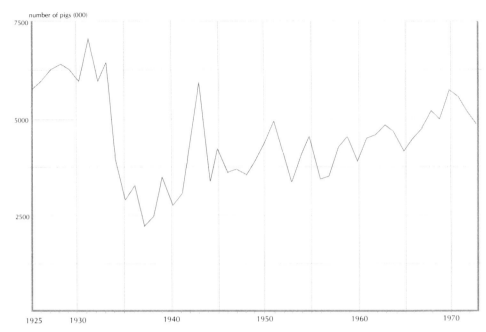

number of pigs (000)

Graph 5.6. PIG CROP (Nebraska State–Federal Division of Agricultural Statistics)

Farm flocks comprise the bulk of Nebraska sheep production.

pig reproduces at a young age, is prolific, and converts feed to meat efficiently, making pork production the most consistently profitable livestock enterprise. These attributes have also allowed pork production to be rather cyclical, swinging rapidly from periods of profit to periods of loss as the supply of pork changes (graph 5.5). The magnitude of these swings can be seen in a comparison of the 1931 pig crop of 7.2 million with the 1937 pig crop of 2.2 million, a 70 percent reduction in six years. While recent cycles have not been as dras-

tic, the state's pig crop dropped from 5.9 million in 1970 to 4.8 million in 1974 (graph 5.6).

Pork production will continue to be concentrated in northeast Nebraska but can be expected to increase outside of that traditional producing area. The increasing pork slaughter capacity in the state will result in an increase in the proportion of hogs sold directly to packers and will create a greater need for timely marketing information.

WILLIAM T. AHLSCHWEDE

Graph 5.7. SHEEP AND LAMBS ON FEED, 1924–73 (Nebraska State–Federal Division of Agricultural Statistics)

SHEEP

Sheep production in Nebraska can be divided into two main categories—feeding lambs for slaughter and raising lambs on farms and ranches. Sheep feeding, in which the state ranks fourth, is concentrated in the Panhandle area. Lamb feeding has declined substantially since the late 1950s (graph 5.7) for several reasons: (1) fewer lambs are being produced in the United States; (2) lamb producers are turning out a higher percentage of fat lambs and fewer feeders; and (3) lamb feeding is a high-risk enterprise. Lambs are fed primarily in drylot in several areas of Nebraska. Some are used to

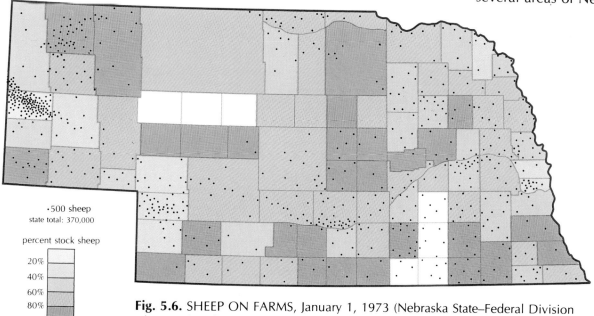

·500 sheep
state total: 370,000

percent stock sheep

20%
40%
60%
80%

less than 1% not indicated

Fig. 5.6. SHEEP ON FARMS, January 1, 1973 (Nebraska State–Federal Division of Agricultural Statistics)

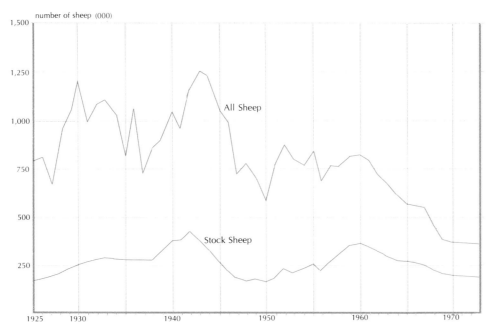

number of sheep (000)

Graph 5.8. SHEEP ON FARMS, January 1, 1973 (Nebraska State–Federal Division of Agricultural Statistics)

glean cornfields after harvest and are finished there or moved to a drylot for a short feed.

The Panhandle has the largest number of stock sheep, although they are widely dispersed across the state (fig. 5.6). The number of sheep in Nebraska declined from a high of 1,265,000 head in 1943 to 330,000 in 1974 (graph 5.8).

Ewe flocks used to be a supplemental source of farm income; but with increasing costs of farming, such small flocks usually make an insignificant contribution to net profits. Thus, there is a trend toward larger, well-managed units that practice confinement production, early weaning, and multiple lambing. Intensive management of larger ewe flocks offers possibilities for profitable returns and increased sheep production in farming areas of the state.

Paul Q. Guyer

POULTRY AND EGGS

The reported gross income from all Nebraska poultry products varies from $15 million to $20 million per year, which represents approximately 1 percent of cash receipts from farm marketings. Over 70 percent of this income is from the sale of eggs. Hatchery receipts add another $1.5 million to $2 million to gross poultry returns. The state's marketing agencies also add to poultry returns. The poultry industry provides a sizable market for the corn, milo, and soybeans produced in the state.

The total laying hen population declined steadily from a high of 18 million in 1944 to 3.6 million in 1974 (graph 5.9). However, those numbers do not adequately tell the trends in the egg industry. A commercial type of industry (one having 10,000 or more hens per flock) began to develop in the late 1950s. By 1960 Nebraska had a total of 100,000 hens in such flocks. Today 2.5 million hens, representing 70 percent of the industry, are in commercial flocks, and the concentration is expected to continue. The remaining 1.1 million laying hens are in flocks of 10–300 hens on general farms. This portion of the industry continues to decline. At same time, the total number of eggs produced per hen has gradually increased (graph 5.10).

The egg industry is concentrated around the major egg markets, in the eastern third of the state (fig. 5.7), where technical services are more readily available, producers can buy feed and pullets more competitively, and hatcheries and feed mills are most abundant (fig. 5.8).

The turkey industry is very specialized, and it is not uncommon for one grower to produce 50,000–150,000 birds per year. The number of growers in the state has decreased but the remaining growers continue to produce larger flocks. Consequently, the total size of the industry (1 million turkeys) has remained relatively constant since the mid-1950s.

There is no commercial broiler industry in Nebraska. Nevertheless, the number of broiler chicks sold annually in the state has gradually increased to about 1.5 million. These birds are raised in small flocks of 20–100 for home and neighborhood consumption. Since portions of the state are not readily served by the large broiler industry, some producers have put broilers in houses that once contained small layer flocks.

Marketing Poultry and Eggs

Although Nebraska imports eggs for processing, the state exports table eggs, those purchased in the shell and used directly by the consumer. These eggs are cleaned, graded, and cartoned by dealers or, in some cases, by the producer. In 1973 the in-state consumption of table eggs was approximately 400 million, and another 200 million were exported.

Nebraska has the largest egg-drying (further processing) industry in the nation. In 1973 over 300 million eggs were imported

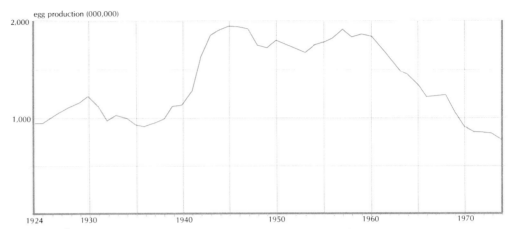

Graph 5.9. EGG PRODUCTION, 1924–73 (Nebraska State–Federal Division of Agricultural Statistics)

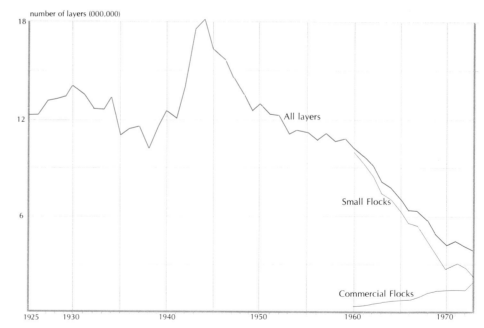

Graph 5.10. NUMBER OF LAYERS, 1925–73 (Nebraska Poultry Industries Office)

89

for this purpose, leaving a net import of about 100 million. The eggs are cleaned, broken, separated into whites and yolks, and some are dried. The total egg market available to Nebraska is over 1 billion eggs, equivalent to egg production from over 5 million hens, or about 1.5 million more than the state is currently raising.

This market availability is one of the reasons for the growth in commercial flocks in the state and is an important factor in the continued growth of the commercial egg industry.

Nebraska ranks fourth among the states in fowl processing. The industry, which imports spent fowl (old layers) from as far away as Washington, Oregon, Texas, and Alabama, provides jobs for many people and a competitive market for the spent fowl from the layer industry.

There is one turkey-processing plant in Nebraska, a cooperative owned by producers in Nebraska and neighboring states. Except for a few that are exported, turkeys move directly to it. In 1973 about half the turkeys it processed were imported. It also processes a few broilers.

EARL W. GLEAVES

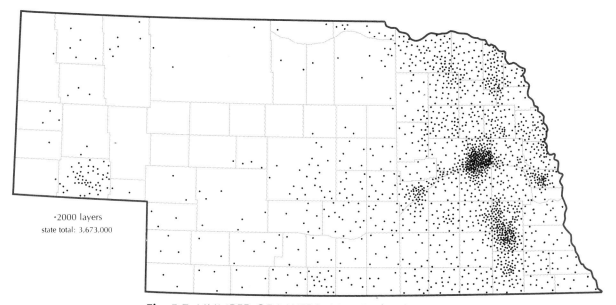

·2000 layers
state total: 3,673,000

Fig. 5.7. NUMBER OF LAYERS, 1973 (Nebraska State–Federal Division of Agricultural Statistics)

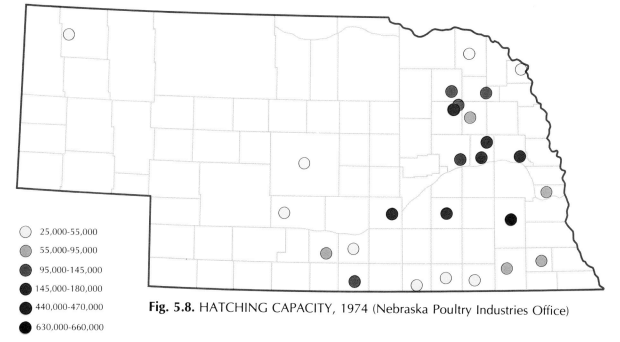

25,000-55,000
55,000-95,000
95,000-145,000
145,000-180,000
440,000-470,000
630,000-660,000

Fig. 5.8. HATCHING CAPACITY, 1974 (Nebraska Poultry Industries Office)

BEEKEEPING

Honeybees were first brought to America by the early colonists. Some escaped, establishing wild colonies that eventually spread across the continent. Indians referred to them as the white man's fly. Since Nebraska was primarily prairie, there was little to attract honeybees until the land was broken up for cultivation.

The use of sweet clover in crop-rotation programs and the use of modern trucks which enabled keepers to operate a larger number of colonies, were probably the two main contributors to the increase in commercial honey production in Nebraska. The primary honey-production area during the 1930s and 1940s was in the eastern one-third of the state; but as commercial fertilizers began to play a more important part in crop production in the 1950s and the growing of sweet clover began to decline, production dropped off there.

The principal honey-production area has moved westward along the Platte valley, where a considerable amount of volunteer sweet clover grows and alfalfa is raised (fig. 5.9). Rainfall is lower in this area and less dryland alfalfa is cut for hay, so more fields are left for seed.

The numerous alfalfa dehydrating plants located in the Platte valley normally contract for a greater amount of alfalfa than they can harvest, especially if they get behind because of rain. When that occurs,

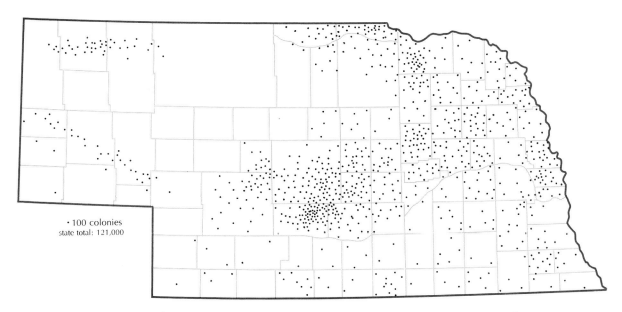

• 100 colonies
state total: 121,000

Fig. 5.9. BEE COLONIES, 1973 (Nebraska Department of Agriculture)

there are some fields of alfalfa in full bloom almost everywhere along the valley and beekeepers are able to secure large amounts of honey.

In the northern part of the Panhandle, alfalfa is commonly grown for seed or is cut for hay under dryland conditions. The regrowth that occurs after hay is cut often blooms and in some years remarkably high yields of alfalfa honey are secured. However, in extremely hot, dry years this area has been known to "burn up," with honeybee colonies making no honey at all.

In the extreme south-central part of the state, the rough lands along the Republican River yield good honey crops from both sweetclover and alfalfa.

The number of honeybee colonies has risen rather sharply, from 49,000 in 1939 to 131,000 in 1974. Part of this large increase—39,000 between 1964 and 1974—can be attributed to the influx of migratory beekeepers seeking to escape spray poisoning of their bees. In some of the warmer areas of the United States, such as California, Texas, and Florida, weekly spraying of certain crops is a common practice. It is difficult to keep bees in such areas since they are vulnerable to the insecticides used. For years losses of bees from insecticides were relatively low in Nebraska; however, more of the state's crops are now being treated, and many of the newer insecticides are more toxic to bees. In 1974, Nebraska beekeepers reported a $120,697.50 loss due to spray poisoning.

The true value of the honeybee is not represented only by the honey and beeswax produced. Honeybees are necessary for the pollination of more than fifty-five different agricultural crops. The use of modern pesticides has destroyed many wild insect pollinators, and honeybees are the only insect that can be moved into areas where crops need pollination.

In 1974, Nebraska beekeepers had 131,000 colonies of bees producing 10,742,000 pounds of honey and 204,000 pounds of beeswax. Not counting the value of the crops pollinated by honeybees, the value of the products provided by the industry was $5,508,380.

The honey marketed in early-day Nebraska was generally the surplus from the few hives that many farmers kept for their own supply. Most of it was in the form of comb honey. Since all honey crystallizes and there is no way to reliquify comb honey without melting the wax, comb honey must be sold and consumed rather rapidly. Today the major portion of the honey produced in Nebraska is extracted and sold in either liquid or granulated form. It does not need to be sold immediately, for if it granulates, it can be restored to its liquid state by heating. Beekeepers normally pack their extracted honey in 60-pound cans or 55-gallon steel drums. When properly sealed and stored, it can be kept for several years.

There are many uses of beeswax, but the largest percentage is converted to wax foundation used by the beekeepers as starters in the frames of their honey super. Two other large users of beeswax are the candle and cosmetic industries.

C. J. WALSTROM

92

6
Agricultural
Economy

Farm Income and Expenses

Not only does the agricultural economy of Nebraska vary from east to west and north to south, but commodity prices and input costs show frequent changes from year to year, as do crop yields and livestock performance. Both yields and rates of livestock production are affected by such factors as weather, disease, and insects, all of which have a direct bearing on the net incomes of Nebraska's farmers and ranchers.

In 1969, Nebraska had a gross farm income of $2.6 billion (fig. 6.1). Of that total, $1.7 billion was from the sale of livestock and livestock products, $534 million was from the sale of crops, and $200 million was in government payments for compliance with national farm programs. The livestock and crop sales do not accurately reflect the value of production of these commodities, however, since a considerable amount of the state's crop and forage production is marketed by feeding livestock and poultry. Approximately 70 percent of the costs incurred in producing livestock is for feed.

Production expenses for Nebraska farmers, which in 1969 were approximately $1.97 billion (fig. 6.1), follow the trends of the general economy. Inflation, increased energy costs, and increased overhead costs have resulted in increased production expenses in recent years.

The net farm income realized by the state's farms and ranches in 1969 was $665 million. From 1967 to 1969 the total net farm income per farm was highest in mid-

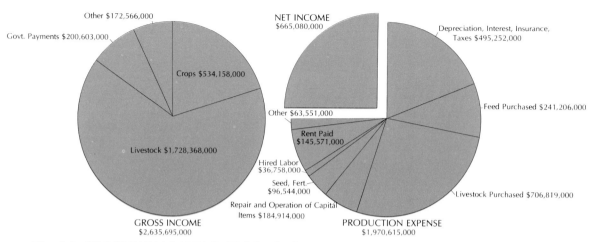

Fig. 6.1. GROSS FARM INCOME, PRODUCTION EXPENSE, AND NET INCOME, 1969 (U.S. Department of Commerce, Social and Economic Statistics Administration)

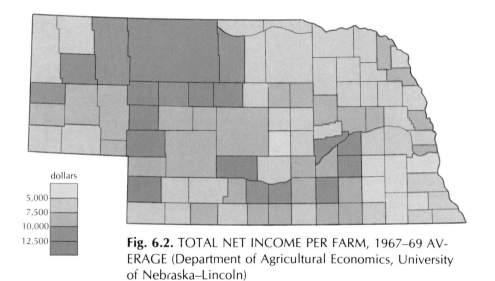

Fig. 6.2. TOTAL NET INCOME PER FARM, 1967–69 AVERAGE (Department of Agricultural Economics, University of Nebraska–Lincoln)

94

Nebraska and the Sandhills area (fig. 6.2) because of the larger size of the operations there. Conversely, farms in southeastern Nebraska, which are generally smaller and produce less for sale, had total net incomes of $7,500 or less per farm during that period.

Land Values

The value of land and buildings per acre in 1969 was highest in about the eastern one-third of the state and in the Scotts Bluff County area (fig. 6.3). This concentration of the average value of land and buildings per acre is related to the intensiveness of the agriculture and the demand for land to accommodate industrial and residential expansion as well as for crop production. The price of land for farming and ranching has increased significantly since 1969, and the construction of more sophisticated buildings for livestock, grain storage, machinery storage, and the like has increased the average value of buildings per acre. The potential for irrigation development has also forced land values up.

The size of farm, quality of land, and irrigation are major factors affecting average per acre values. For example, relatively large ranching units are found in the Cherry County area; and the urban growth and population concentration which have occurred in Douglas and Sarpy Counties in eastern Nebraska and in Scotts Bluff County in western Nebraska have a direct influence on the value of the land and buildings per farm (fig. 6.4)

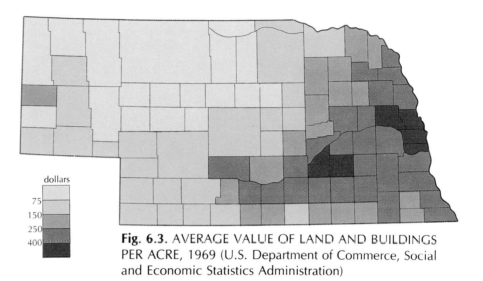

Fig. 6.3. AVERAGE VALUE OF LAND AND BUILDINGS PER ACRE, 1969 (U.S. Department of Commerce, Social and Economic Statistics Administration)

dollars
75
150
250
400

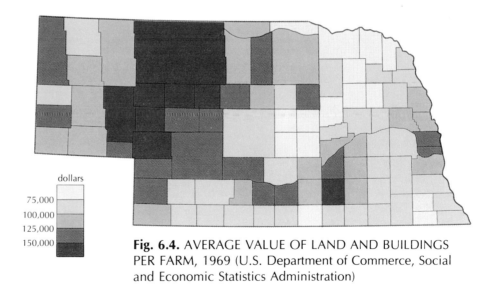

Fig. 6.4. AVERAGE VALUE OF LAND AND BUILDINGS PER FARM, 1969 (U.S. Department of Commerce, Social and Economic Statistics Administration)

dollars
75,000
100,000
125,000
150,000

Farm Financing

Farming and ranching in Nebraska require large amounts of capital. Investments in farms of one-fourth to one-half million dollars and more are common, and an operating capital of $30,000 or more a year is often needed. Beef feedlots require extremely large amounts of operating capital for feeder animals, feed, and other operational costs.

As of January 1, 1974, a total of $1.6 billion worth of non–real estate Nebraska farm loans were held by principal lending institutions—$1.26 billion worth by commercial banks, $341 million worth by the production credit associations, and $15.7 million worth by the Farmers Home Administration (fig. 6.5).

The total farm real estate debt increased from about $350 million in 1960 to $1.5 billion in 1974. In 1974, the largest holders of farm real estate debt were individuals, followed by the federal land banks and life insurance companies. The active involvement of individuals as farm real estate lenders indicates increased contract sales of farm land and buildings (graph 6.1).

Hired Farm Labor and Custom Work Expense

In addition to the operator and family labor used on farms and ranches, hired farm labor and custom operator services make a considerable contribution to the state's agricultural economy. Custom work expenses include charges for machines used and the

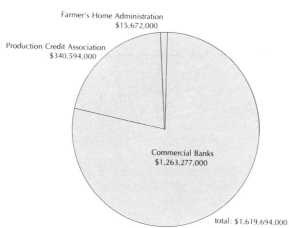

Fig. 6.5. NON–REAL ESTATE FARM LOANS: Amounts Held by Principal Lending Institutions, January 1, 1974 (U.S. Department of Agriculture)

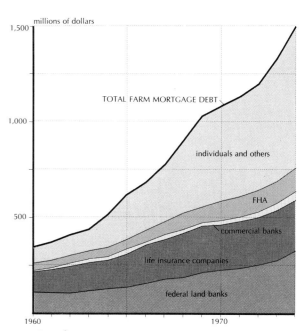

Graph 6.1. NEBRASKA FARM REAL ESTATE DEBT (U.S. Department of Agriculture)

96

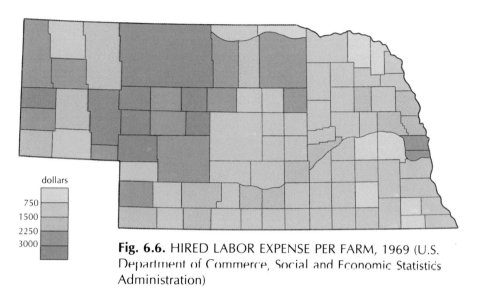

Fig. 6.6. HIRED LABOR EXPENSE PER FARM, 1969 (U.S. Department of Commerce, Social and Economic Statistics Administration)

dollars
750
1500
2250
3000

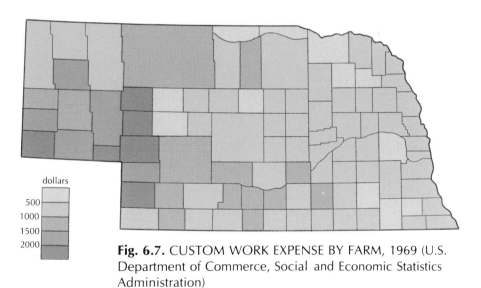

Fig. 6.7. CUSTOM WORK EXPENSE BY FARM, 1969 (U.S. Department of Commerce, Social and Economic Statistics Administration)

dollars
500
1000
1500
2000

labor required to operate and service them. The average hired farm labor expense per farm in 1969 was largest for farms in the Sandhills, the Panhandle, and southwestern Nebraska (fig. 6.6), where it appears to be related to the operation of relatively large cattle ranches.

Nebraska's agriculture is highly mechanized. Tractors, machines, and electricity have replaced to a large extent the animal and human physical labor on farms. The farmer has the alternatives of owning machines, leasing them, trading off machine work with his neighbors, or hiring custom operators to perform some of his machine work. The services of custom operators are used across the state, particularly for harvesting, but also in tillage, planting, spraying, hauling, and other operations. Custom work expenses per farm in 1969 were higher for the southern one-half of the Panhandle and southwestern Nebraska than in the remainder of the state (fig. 6.7), reflecting the use of custom operators on wheat farms, especially for the harvest.

Volume of Business

The net income realized by farmers and ranchers is dependent upon the volume of sales per farm and the net income realized per crop, animal, or other product sold. In terms of economic size classes Nebraska's farms and ranches are becoming larger. There were 3,741 farms, or 4.1 percent, in economic size class I in 1959. By 1969 the number had reached 10,570 farms, or 14.6

percent (table 6.1). This increase in size has come about by both "push" and "pull" forces. Larger farms have the opportunity to realize larger total net incomes. Moreover, increasing costs and narrowing profit margins had had a "push" influence on farms to become larger if they are to remain in business. Unless there are nonfarm sources of income, only class I and class II size farms are large enough with current price-cost relationships to provide a family living income and to make payments on the capital investment required for farming.

Class I and II farms and ranches, which make up 36.6 percent of the total in the state, accounted for 81.8 percent of the value of all farm products produced in Nebraska in 1969 (table 6.2). By comparison, in 1959 class I and class II farms produced 50.2 percent of the value of farm products. Since farms and ranches vary considerably in terms of intensity of production, the value of products sold per farm is useful in illustrating economic size differences.

GLEN VOLLMAR

Table 6.1. Number of Farms in Nebraska by Economic Size Classes for 1959, 1969, and Projected to 1979

Size Class (Annual Sales per Farm)	1959	1969	1979
	%	%	
Class I ($40,000 and over)	3,741 (4.1)	10,570 (14.6)	18,000
Class II ($20,000–$39,999)	9,033 (10.0)	15,902 (22.0)	12,000
Class III ($10,000–$19,999)	22,808 (25.3)	17,691 (24.5)	13,200
Class IV ($5,000–$9,000)	26,485 (29.4)	12,114 (16.8)	6,000
Class V ($2,500–$4,999)	15,263 (16.9)	7,108 (9.8)	3,300
	77,330 (100.0)	63,385 (100.0)	52,500

Source: U.S. Census Data and projection to 1979 by University of Nebraska–Lincoln agricultural specialists.

Table 6.2. Average Value of Products Sold per Farm by Economic Size Classes and Percentage of Total Sales in Each Size Class, 1959 and 1969

Size Class (Annual Sales per Farm)	1959	1969
Class I ($40,000 and over)	$95,611 (29.8%)	$126,112 (61.3%)
Class II ($20,000–$39,999)	27,107 (20.4%)	27,984 (20.5%)
Class III ($10,000–$19,999)	14,081 (26.8%)	14,364 (12.0%)
Class IV ($ 5,000 to $ 9,000)	7,501 (16.6%)	7,429 (4.2%)
Class V ($ 2,500 to $ 4,999)	3,914 (5.0%)	3,658 (1.2%)

Source: U.S. Census Data.

7
Marketing

Livestock Marketing
Dairy Marketing
Grain Marketing

LIVESTOCK MARKETING

Livestock marketing is tremendously important in Nebraska because of the large numbers and high value of the cattle, hogs, and sheep produced in the state. Moreover, the marketing of meat and livestock products by the packing and processing industries of Nebraska adds significantly to the state's agricultural economy.

Livestock marketing has changed dramatically since 1955, although less in the location of public markets (figs. 7.1 and 7.2) than in the usage (fig. 7.3). The building of several rural packing plants in the central and eastern parts of the state has influenced the marketing patterns significantly.

Direct purchases of slaughter livestock by packers have increased markedly (fig. 7.3), forcing livestock producers to gather market information so they can market their livestock wisely. The use of commission men to sell slaughter livestock has declined slowly for several years. More and more livestock are being marketed on a carcass basis, but the majority is still sold on a live-weight basis.

Generally, meat rather than live slaughter animals is shipped by truck from Nebraska to the major East and West Coast consumption areas. Meat is shipped in two forms, hanging in carcasses, or in boxes. The use of piggyback rail service for shipping meat may increase in the future.

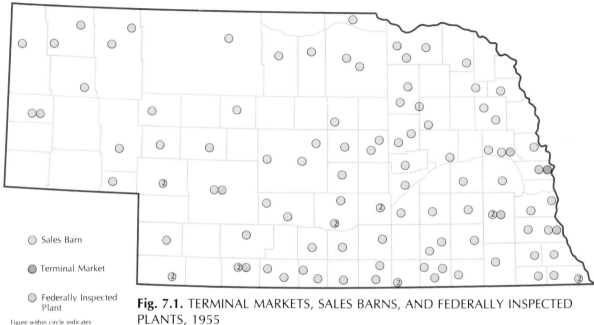

Sales Barn

Terminal Market

Federally Inspected Plant

Figure within circle indicates number if greater than one.

Fig. 7.1. TERMINAL MARKETS, SALES BARNS, AND FEDERALLY INSPECTED PLANTS, 1955

Data are not readily available on changes in buying and selling methods for breeding and feeder livestock, although the bulk of it is still bought and sold through direct person-to-person negotiation or through order buyers and livestock dealers. Large numbers of feeder pigs and feeder cattle and calves still move through the local auction market.

Feeder pig cooperatives that farrow large numbers of pigs have started operations recently. Most of the feeder pigs produced are sold directly to the members of the cooperative instead of through other market outlets.

Since 1950 hog slaughter has fluctuated but mostly increased; the sheep and lamb slaughter has generally declined; and cattle slaughter has rapidly increased, so that the total number of livestock slaughtered in the state has grown considerably (fig. 7.4). Market receipts in Nebraska have also increased since 1950 (fig. 7.5). These trends of increasing numbers of livestock marketed and slaughtered are likely to continue.

Fed cattle marketed from all feedlots numbered 1,822,000 head in 1962 and 3,355,000 head in 1974. The number of

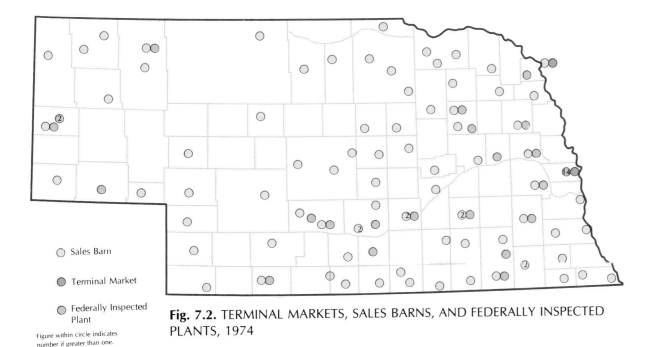

Sales Barn

Terminal Market

Federally Inspected Plant

Figure within circle indicates number if greater than one.

Fig. 7.2. TERMINAL MARKETS, SALES BARNS, AND FEDERALLY INSPECTED PLANTS, 1974

feedlots declined from 24,303 in 1962 to 14,970 in 1974, but the number of feedlots exceeding 1,000 head capacity increased from 312 to 460 during the same period. Marketings from feedlots under 1,000 head capacity accounted for 73 percent of the total marketings in 1962 but only 40 percent of the total in 1974. Similar marketing data are not available for hogs and sheep.

The addition of two new hog-slaughtering plants in the state will sharply increase the state's hog-slaughtering capacity by 1976. It is likely that hogs will then move into Nebraska to be slaughtered as cattle now do.

The importance of Nebraska's livestock producing, marketing, and meat-packing industry is clearly borne out by its national rank in several livestock categories: in 1974 the state led in commercial cattle slaughter

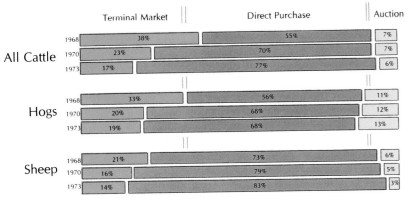

Fig. 7.3. PURCHASES OF SLAUGHTER LIVESTOCK BY PACKERS FOR SELECTED YEARS (Nebraska State–Federal Division of Agricultural Statistics)

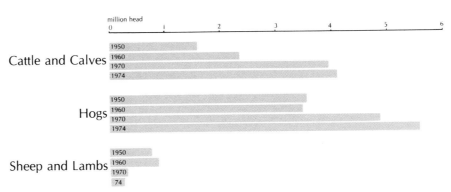

Fig. 7.4. COMMERCIAL SLAUGHTER OF LIVESTOCK FOR SELECTED YEARS (Nebraska State–Federal Division of Agricultural Statistics)

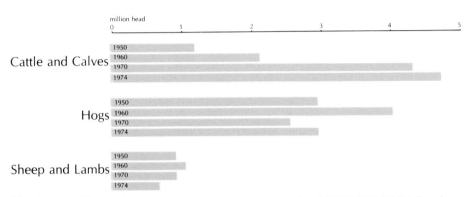

Fig. 7.5. MARKET RECEIPTS OF LIVESTOCK FOR SELECTED YEARS (Nebraska State–Federal Division of Agricultural Statistics)

and ranked second in several other categories, including the value of all cattle and calves on farms; heifers 500 pounds and over; fed cattle and calves marketed; and commercial livestock slaughter, all species. Nebraska is also one of the top six states in the nation in several other important livestock rankings.

Trends for all three livestock classes will depend on future United States agricultural and economic policy, the energy situation, feed and forage prices and availability, and mother nature. External forces may have a greater influence on the livestock industry than the decisions of individual Nebraska livestock producers.

ALLEN C. WELLMAN

DAIRY MARKETING

Nebraska's earliest settlers were concerned with a dependable source of milk and dairy products. Since there were no dairy stores or supermarkets where the housewife could purchase a carton of fresh milk, a pound of butter, or a package of cheddar cheese, each family had to provide its own source of these foods. As they traveled to and through present-day Nebraska they drove their milk cows with them.

It was not until 1860 that cheese or butter was manufactured commercially in the state. In that year there was a modest commercial cheese-making operation near Brownville and during the later 1860s a cheese factory of considerable size was built at Palmyra. From these modest beginnings a fairly sizable cheese industry developed and by 1895 there were fifteen cheese plants located in Nebraska. About that time, however, the introduction of the farm cream separator resulted in the demise of the cheese industry. Rather than sell their whole milk to a cheese factory, farmers preferred to separate the milk on the farm, market the cream, and use the skim milk as animal feed.

Since the turn of the century, the state's dairy industry has been most noted for the amount of butter it produced. In 1929, nearly 100 million pounds of butter was produced by creameries, almost all of it from

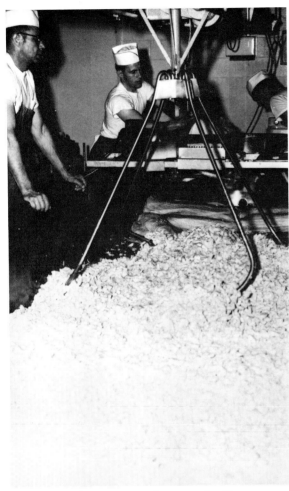

Cheese production, a major use of milk produced in Nebraska.

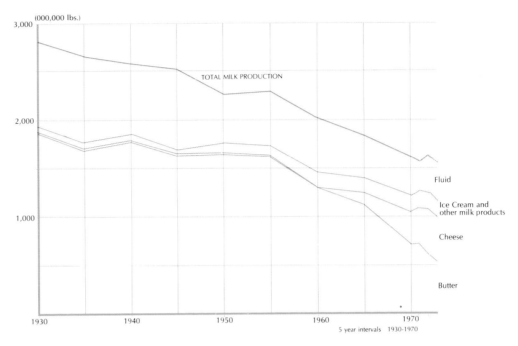

Graph 7.1. USE OF MILK, 1930–73 (U.S. Department of Agriculture)

farm-separated cream. That represented nearly 85 percent of all the milk marketed in the state that year. For twenty years, from 1941 until 1960, Nebraska was the fourth-ranking state in the production of butter.

During the early 1960s, however, a change occurred in the marketing of milk (graph 7.1). Skim milk was valued less as an animal feed, and farmers quit using the cream separator. The butter industry was hurt by the widespread acceptance of margarine; meanwhile, the per capita consumption of cheese was increasing, favoring the re-establishment of the cheese industry. A number of cheese plants were opened, principally in central and northeastern Nebraska, and farmers turned to selling whole milk (fig. 7.6). From 1965 to 1975 the production of butter declined steadily while cheese production increased sharply.

In 1973, the state's creameries produced less than 23 million pounds of butter, most of it from factory-separated cream, and the twelve cheese factories turned out over 66 million pounds of cheese. This compares

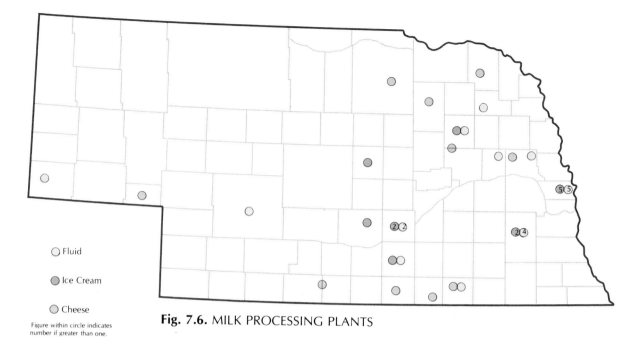

Fig. 7.6. MILK PROCESSING PLANTS

with less than a million pounds in 1961. Other markets for Nebraska milk in 1973 included about 135 million pounds used in ice cream and other frozen desserts, and nearly 500 million pounds sold as fresh whole milk, low-fat milk, skim milk, cream, half and half and flavored milk drinks.

T. ALLEN EVANS

GRAIN MARKETING

The grain elevator industry in Nebraska can trace its beginnings to the late 1800s. As a result of increased production of grains, government storage programs, improved harvesting techniques, better highways, larger trucks, changes in rail service, and the introduction of artificial grain drying, however, the local grain elevators of that earlier time are now complete farm service centers. Today they are diversified businesses offering complete grain-marketing services plus feed, fertilizer, agricultural chemicals, petroleum products, hardware, and, in some cases, farm machinery and lumber.

Many of the early elevators in the state were line elevators owned by large national or international grain concerns, so called because they were managed from offices located at major grain terminal markets like Chicago, Omaha, and Kansas City. The name "line elevator" referred to their location at regular intervals along a railroad line. The farmers' elevator movement, originated in the early 1900s as a protest against market control by the large grain companies, resulted in the establishment of many of the farmer-owned grain cooperatives operating in the state today.

The earliest grain elevators stored very little grain but provided handling facilities for the local farmers. With the expansion of grain-production capacity and the institution of government price-support programs in the 1950s and 1960s, grain storage became an important function of the industry. To accommodate the growing reserves of wheat and feed grains, the Commodity Credit Corporation of the United States Department of Agriculture encouraged the construction of commercial grain elevator capacity during the 1950s and 1960s, offering low-interest loans and accelerated depreciation schedules as incentives. During that period, Nebraska's commercial grain-storage capacity grew rapidly. Changes in government price-support programs in the late 1960s put greater emphasis on acreage restriction and seemed to suggest that the grain elevator industry might be overbuilt. However, continued irrigation development and the introduction of more rapid harvesting equipment encouraged further expansion of the industry. Fifty million bushels of commercial grain-storage space, representing a 12 percent increase, were added in the state from 1960 to 1973.

The total commercial grain-storage capacity was 453.5 million bushels in 1973 (fig. 7.7). Of that, approximately 85 million bushels' capacity was in terminal or subterminal elevators. Douglas, Lancaster, and Adams Counties are the primary centers of terminal and subterminal elevators, with 30, 29, and 25 million bushels of storage space, respectively. There is an additional 1.5 million bushels' capacity in Buffalo County.

On-farm grain-storage and drying capacity has also been increased as the result of more rapid grain harvesting and expanded acreage. With the transition to combines for harvesting feed grains, the traditional corn crib for ear corn was replaced by grain bins and high-moisture grain storage on farms. Today many farmers have the equivalent of small grain elevators, complete with dump pits for unloading trucks, legs for elevating grain, a considerable amount of bin space, augers for emptying bins, scales for weighing, and dryers for conditioning grain. The total on-farm grain-storage capacity in Nebraska is approximately 800 million bushels, with 100 million bushels of ear corn storage representing about 12 percent of the total. In 1973 on-farm storage capacity was equal to 95 percent of the small grain and row crop production, and in 1974 there were 34,000 grain dryers on the state's farms, an increase of 70 percent from 1968.

The grain industry has continued to rely heavily upon railroads to move grain from rural areas to terminal destinations. As a

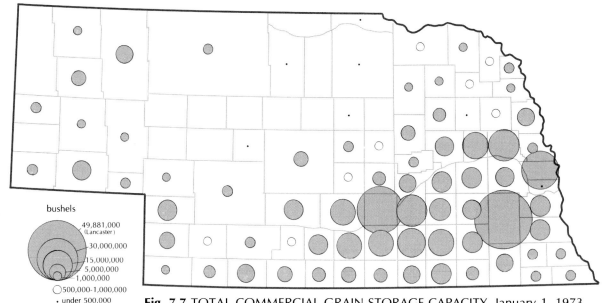

Fig. 7.7 TOTAL COMMERCIAL GRAIN STORAGE CAPACITY, January 1, 1973 (Nebraska State Agricultural Stabilization and Conservation Service)

major grain-producing state, Nebraska is put at a disadvantage by its remoteness from major domestic and export markets. This explains in part the importance of the state's livestock production and feeding industry. In spite of the large feeding industry within the state, however, nearly one-half of the feed grain production leaves the state to be fed in other areas of the country or to be exported.

Most of Nebraska's exported grain moves through Gulf port terminals, with some limited amounts (primarily of wheat) shipped from Pacific Coast ports.

The expanded cattle-feeding industries in Texas, Oklahoma, and Colorado have become increasingly important markets for Ne-

braska feed grains. Most of the grain destined for those feedlots moves by truck. The increased use of trucks to ship grain has been welcomed by the state's grain industry, particularly during periods of severe railcar shortages.

In the future even more of the grain will be moved directly from farms to primary markets or final destinations and the result may be significant reductions in freight rates for unit train (fifty-car) shipments. Subterminal elevators receiving grain from both local elevators and farmers are of growing importance because they can accommodate unit train shipments and benefit from the lower freight rates.

Soybean Processing

Soybeans are a relatively new crop to Nebraska and it was not until the 1950s that production expanded to the point of supporting commercial processing in the state. In 1950, two processing plants with a combined capacity of approximately 100 tons of soybeans per day were located in Nebraska, and by 1973 the state had five processing facilities with a daily capacity of 1,475 tons. The soybean-processing industry is concentrated in the eastern part of the state, where most of the soybeans are produced.

The current processing capacity exceeds the total annual production of soybeans in the state; and while a portion of Nebraska's crop continues to be processed in neighboring states, soybeans are also brought into the state for processing. Because of technological advances in soybean processing, new plants must be large to achieve efficient operation. The most recently constructed plant tripled the state's processing capacity. With the continued expansion of soybean production in Nebraska and neighboring soybean-producing states, additional facilities will be needed.

The products of soybean processing include soybean oil, which is used in both food and manufactured products and much of which is shipped to other states or exported to foreign countries, and soybean meal, a high-protein feed supplement used extensively by livestock and commercial feed industries.

Flour Milling

Although Nebraska ranks fourth in winter wheat production, flour milling is not a major agricultural industry. In 1973, the state's six flour mills processed 17.9 million bushels of wheat and produced 7.7 million hundredweights of flour. Generally, between one-fifth and one-sixth of Nebraska's wheat crop is processed within the state.

The lack of interest in constructing more flour mills in Nebraska and other wheat-producing states of the Great Plains is due primarily to the railroads' practice of offering transit rates for rail shipment of wheat. A transit rate is a combination freight rate permitting raw material like wheat to be stopped en route for processing or storage and to be reshipped at a favorable rate to a final destination; hence it favors those flour mills located between the major production areas and the eastern population centers.

MICHAEL S. TURNER

8
The Outlook for
the Future

An agricultural atlas provides a panorama of the past and present features of the state's agricultural resources, economy, and development. It gives us a set of reference points against which we can measure future change. Having defined the many geographical bench marks characterizing agriculture, it is appropriate to turn toward the future and speculate on the changes that may be in store. Nebraska's agriculture is not static; it is a dynamic industry subject to continual change.

A number of factors influence the course of the state's agricultural development. In the first place, Nebraska's agriculture is part of a national agricultural economy and, beyond that, of a world agricultural economy. Nationally, we have passed from a situation in which we were concerned with food surpluses to one in which reduced inventories and higher prices have become topics of popular concern. The American consumer has discovered somewhat to his chagrin that he competes with foreign consumers for the products of Nebraska's agriculture.

It would be foolhardy to suggest that we have seen the last of the crop surpluses which characterized so much of the past decades. However, on balance, it appears that agriculture will be confronted with relatively more favorable economic circumstances as we look ahead to 1985 than in the past. The United States population continues to increase, albeit at a slow pace, and the economy will continue to gain, if unevenly. Both of these factors translate into greater consumption of food. Beyond that, increases in the population and expenditures for food in the other developed countries will contribute to a growing demand for the products of the state's agriculture.

Nebraska has a strong competitive position in the agricultural economy. It is an efficient producer of crop and livestock products and has the potential for further development of its natural resources and agricultural production plant. In the face of a national land base whose potential for further development grows more limited, Nebraska's favored agricultural position should continue to improve.

On the other hand, factors which have a dampening effect on agricultural growth and development must be recognized. In the future the higher cost of energy will be translated into higher production costs. Consequently, there may be some tendency to shift toward those enterprises and production methods which use more labor and less capital. Chemical fertilizers and pesticides have become higher priced and may remain so, creating the incentive to economize on them. Environmental constraints also tend to slow development and increase production costs. Increases in crop yields, and livestock productivity depend on new technologies— the results of research and education. Such increases will require more effort, and will come at higher cost, than in the past.

In sum, I am suggesting that future agricultural atlases will be different from the present one. We should recognize that the changes we will observe will come, not automatically, but rather as the result of the efforts of a good many organizations and people. First, the operators and managers of farms and ranches will make use of new knowledge, methods, and tools in their operations. Manufacturers of farm supplies, marketers of agricultural products, finance agencies, and others providing goods and services to the industry will have new products and new services with which to serve the industry better. Standing back of all of them will be those whose role it is to provide new agricultural knowledge and techniques. The Agricultural Experiment Station conducts research at strategic locations throughout the state. The data and ideas from that research are carried to users by the Agricultural Extension Service. Providing a pool of trained people for the agricultural industry is the College of Agriculture, with both its collegiate program and its technical program at the School of Technical Agriculture at Curtis. The Conservation and Survey Division and the Water Resources Research Institute provide data and service in the areas of natural resources, soil, and water. Other units of the University of Nebraska provide assistance to the agricultural industry as well.

The State Department of Agriculture provides regulatory and other kinds of assistance important to the industry. The Department of Economic Development assists agricultural input, marketing, or processing firms considering Nebraska locations. The Natural Resources Commission and Department of Water Resources assist in the development of water and other natural resources on which agriculture depends.

Likewise, United States Department of Agriculture agencies provide assistance. The

Agricultural Research Service conducts valuable research on agricultural problems relating to crop and livestock production. The Economic Research Service provides economic information. The Statistical Reporting Service provides agricultural production estimates and other outlook information. The Soil Conservation Service provides technical assistance in conserving soil and water on farms and ranches, while the Agricultural Stabilization Service provides financial assistance for such practices. A number of other USDA agencies also contribute.

Other federal agencies, such as the Reclamation Bureau and Geological Survey in the U.S. Department of Interior, the National Weather Service, and the U.S. Department of Transportation, also provide assistance in agricultural development.

What changes do we visualize in the agricultural atlas of 1985? People are fascinated by projections; one danger is placing too much confidence in them. The following projections are made with the usual qualifications that they are judgments only, and are as fallible and subject to error as other human judgments.[1]

We visualize Nebraska commercial farms and ranches continuing to increase in size

1. These projections are drawn from reports from a major analysis of the future potential of the state's agricultural industry and economy recently completed in the Institute of Agriculture and Natural Resources. This effort, called STAR, involved University staff, members of state agencies and others. A summary report "STAR, Nebraska Agriculture 1980 to 1985" is available from the Institute of Agriculture and Natural Resources, University of Nebraska.

and decrease in number—from 63,000 in 1969 to fewer than 50,000 by 1985. These farms will tend to become more specialized. They will require larger amounts of capital and will place a premium on good management as more sophisticated technologies become part of the business. The output per hour of labor is expected to be 75 percent higher in 1985 than in 1970. More farms will be partnerships or two-operator farms. However, most farms will continue to be family operations.

We expect to see further development of crop production in the future. Nebraska will continue to be an important producer of wheat for domestic use and export, producing over 110 million bushels by 1985, compared to the average of 90 million bushels in 1965–74. Yields will average 48 bushels by 1985, compared to 33 bushels in 1965–74. The acreage devoted to wheat will increase slightly. Higher yields will come about through the introduction of new varieties, disease and insect control, and crop management. The wheat of 1985 will be higher in protein and general nutritional content as a result of the current research effort on these factors.

Soybean acreage is expected to increase by 20 percent to 1.5 million acres by 1985, while yields will increase to 35 bushels from 30 bushels in 1973. This yield increase will result from the planting of improved varieties, better harvesting practices, and other production technologies. It appears that the demand for soybeans will remain strong during this period.

Corn production is expected to double by

1985 as the result of an increase in average yield from 87 bushels to 122 bushels, and the addition of 2.3 million acres, mostly irrigated. Sixty percent of the corn acreage will be irrigated by 1985. Sorghum production is expected to increase by 45 percent by 1985 because of an increase in average yield of 40 percent from 59 bushels to 75 bushels, and the addition of a million acres to the crop. Although the yield of oats will increase also, its acreage will remain relatively constant.

The acreage of grassland in Nebraska will probably decline somewhat by 1985 to make way for crop production and irrigation development. However, the productivity of forages will increase as the result of the planting of 1.5 million acres of improved pastures, better management of grasslands, and the harvesting and use of crops and residues not used for feed. The yields of hay, particularly irrigated alfalfa and wild hay, will increase significantly, perhaps 30 percent and 60 percent, respectively.

The use of silage crops is expected to increase dramatically by 1985, with over a million acres harvested, compared to 650,000 in 1973. Fourteen million tons, mostly corn silage, will be harvested, compared to 8.3 million tons in 1973.

Several general factors will contribute to increased crop production. Six million acres of land will be irrigated in 1985, compared to 4 million in 1971, mostly through the further development of pump irrigation. The quality and value of grain will be improved by improved drying and handling practices and the development of better grain driers.

Nebraska is in a strong position to increase its share of the nation's beef production. Our projections indicate the opportunity for a growth rate of fed cattle 20 percent above the national trend and of cow herd 5 percent above the national trend in 1985. Nebraska will continue to be a leading cattle state because of its feed supply, slaughter capacity, moderate climate, and experienced cattle feeders and ranchers. Improvements in range land management, productivity of forage crops, and yields of grain crops will contribute to improved efficiency of beef production. Other opportunities for improvement lie in improving the ratio of lean to fat in beef carcasses, in the utilization of crossbreeding, in improved reproductive efficiency, and in control of diseases like calf scours, shipping fever, and respiratory diseases.

Nebraska's hog production is expected to increase 40–50 percent by 1985. Pork production will remain concentrated in northeastern Nebraska, but will increase outside of that area as well. The trend toward fewer but larger production units, with an increase in confinement and in the use of mechanized and automated building systems will continue.

Changes will affect other agricultural enterprises as well. Although the number of dairy cows will decrease, the production per cow will increase by 10 percent by 1985. The 1985 laying flock may reach 5.3 million hens, compared to 3.7 million in 1973. Specialty crops—beans, beets, and potatoes—should become more important in the upper Platte valley. There is a strong potential for the expansion of the food-processing industry in the state.

This brief excursion into the future of Nebraska's agriculture illustrates the dynamic nature of the industry. Continued growth and development is in store; the agricultural sector will continue to undergird the state's economy and society.

HOWARD W. OTTOSON